The Supporters' Guide to Non-League Football 1996

EDITOR
John Robinson

Fourth Edition

CONTENTS

British Library Cataloguing in Publication Data
A catalogue record for this book is available from the British Library
ISBN 0-947808-49-3

Copyright © 1995; SOCCER BOOK PUBLISHING LTD. (01472-696226)
72, St. Peters' Avenue, Cleethorpes, Sth. Humberside, DN35 8HU, England

Printed by Adlard Print & Typesetting Services, The Old School, The Green, Ruddington, Notts. NG11 6HH

FOREWORD

Our thanks go to the numerous club officials who have aided us in the compilation of the information contained in this guide and also to Michael Robinson (page layouts), Chris Ambler (photos) and Ceri Sampson (cover artwork) for the part they have played. We are also indebted to the secretaries of the various leagues for providing statistical information and extensive support.

In addition, we wish to thank Tony Williams of the major Non-League football monthly TEAM TALK for the information about the pyramid which appears on page 4.

Although we use the term 'Child' for concessionary prices, this is usually the price charged to Senior Citizens also. We welcome comments from readers as to items which they feel should be included in future editions.

Disabled supporters should note that we have, in conjunction with Shoot magazine, produced an entirely separate booklet, listing relevant information for all of the major League and Non-League clubs in Britain. This is priced at just 99p per copy and can be obtained post free from the address below.

Finally, we would like to wish our readers a happy and safe spectating season.

John Robinson

EDITOR

THE PYRAMID

The concept of the 'Pyramid' has invigorated Non-League football over the past decade, especially now that the G.M. Vauxhall Conference champions are promoted automatically to the Third Division of the Football League (subject to ground standards). Instead of being involved in local isolated competitions, clubs can now see themselves in a national context.

The G.M. Vauxhall Conference is the top rung of the Pyramid. The second rung accommodates the ICIS, Beazer Homes and Unibond Premier Leagues, and these three competitions can be seen as the top rung in each of three regional branches that are fully explained below.

Whilst not common, it is not unheard of for clubs to switch from one branch of the Pyramid to another, especially in 'grey areas' where clubs are torn between two branches. Typical examples have been Boston switching from the Websters Central Midlands to the United Counties League, Viking Sports moving from Hellenic to the Dan-Air, and Wigston Fields and Barlestone St. Giles leaving the Leicestershire League for the Influence Combination.

THE ICIS (ISTHMIAN) BRANCH

There are four leagues officially recognised as feeders to the ICIS Third Division; the Dan-Air, the Essex Senior, the South Midlands (two divisions), and the London Spartan (three divisions). Because the ICIS has four divisions, a club progressing from one of its feeders would need to win two more promotions than a like club in either the Beazer Branch or Northern Premier branch. The ICIS Section is the most flexible in that the additional feeders are not rigidly tied to any one of the leagues above them.

BEAZER HOMES (SOUTHERN) BRANCH

This is the broadest of the three branches. There are no fewer than nine leagues officially feeding the Southern and Midland Divisions of the Beazer, and as for the most part these leagues have promotion/relegation arrangements with local leagues, this is arguably the most complete section of the Pyramid. Over the past couple of seasons, the Beazer Homes League has tightened up its ground facilities requirements, so promotion within the League and from its feeders has not been automatic. The nine feeders are also introducing strict facilities codes; the Wessex, Eastern and Great Mills League all insist on Premier Division grounds being floodlit, and the United Counties and Sussex Leagues will follow suit shortly.

THE UNIBOND (NORTHERN PREMIER) BRANCH

In 1991, the Northern League joined the Carling North West Counties and the Northern Counties (East) Leagues as a third official feeder to the Northern Premier League Division One. This development has had the effect of incorporating the North East in the Pyramid structure because two of the area's prominent competitions, the Northern Alliance and the Wearside League, have negotiated to become official feeder to the Northern League. The Northern Premier branch contains a very contentious 'grey area'; the East Midlands/South Yorkshire region. The Whitebread County, West Yorks and West Riding Leagues slot in under the Northern Counties (East) League, but the Notts. Alliance, Central Midlands and Leicestershire Senior Leagues are torn between the Beazer and Northern Premier branches, and therefore remain outside the official Pyramid.

ALTRINCHAM FC

Founded: 1903	**Colours**: Shirts - Red and White Stripes
Limited Company: 1921	Shorts - Black
Former Name(s): None	**Telephone No.**: (0161) 928-1045
Nickname: 'The Robins'	**Daytime Phone No.**: (0161) 928-1045
Ground: Moss Lane, Altrincham, Greater	**Pitch Size**: 115 × 70yds
Manchester WA15 8AP	**Ground Capacity**: 3,000
Record Attendance: 10,275 (February 1925)	**Seating Capacity**: 1,000

GENERAL INFORMATION
Supporters Club Administrator: -
Address: -
Telephone Number: -
Car Parking: Adjacent
Coach Parking: By Police Direction
Nearest Railway Station: Altrincham (5 minutes walk)
Nearest Bus Station: Altrincham
Club Shop:
Opening Times: Matchdays Only
Telephone No.: (0161) 928-1045
Postal Sales: Yes
Nearest Police Station: Dunham Road, Altrincham
Police Force: Greater Manchester
Police Telephone No.: (0161) 872-5050

GROUND INFORMATION
Away Supporters' Entrances: Chequers End Turnstiles
Away Supporters' Sections: Chequers End of Ground
Family Facilities: **Location of Stand**: No special facilities
Capacity of Stand: -

ADMISSION INFO (1995/96 PRICES)
Adult Standing: £5.50
Adult Seating: £6.50
Child Standing: £3.50
Child Seating: £4.50
Programme Price: £1.00
FAX Number: (0161) 926-9934

POPULAR SIDE

GOLF ROAD END

CHEQUERS END (Away)

MAIN STAND
MOSS LANE

Travelling Supporters Information:
Routes: Exit M56 junction 7 following signs Hale and Altrincham. Through 1st set of traffic lights and take 3rd right - Westminster Road and continue into Moss Lane. Ground on right.

BATH CITY FC

Founded: 1889	**Colours**: Shirts - Black & White Stripes
Former Name(s): None	Shorts - Black
Nickname: 'City'	**Telephone No.**: (01225) 423087
Ground: Twerton Park, Bath BA2 1DB	**Daytime Phone No.**: (01225) 423087
Record Attendance: 18,020 (1960)	**Pitch Size**: 110 × 76yds
	Ground Capacity: 8,943
	Seating Capacity: 1,006

GENERAL INFORMATION
Supporters Club Administrator:
Mr. P. Cater
Address: c/o Club
Telephone Number: (01225) 313247
Car Parking: 150 spaces at Ground
Coach Parking: Avon Street, Bath
Nearest Railway Station: Bath Spa
(1.5 miles)
Nearest Bus Station: Avon Street, Bath
Club Shop:
Opening Times: Matchdays Only
Telephone No.: (01225) 423087
Postal Sales: Yes
Nearest Police Station: Bath (1.5 miles)
Police Force: Avon & Somerset
Police Telephone No.: (01225) 842439

GROUND INFORMATION
Away Supporters' Entrances: Bristol End
Away Supporters' Sections: Bristol End
Family Facilities: **Location of Stand**:
No special facilities
Capacity of Stand: -

ADMISSION INFO (1995/96 PRICES)
Adult Standing: £5.00
Adult Seating: £6.00
Child Standing: £3.00
Child Seating: £4.00
Programme Price: £1.00
FAX Number: (01225) 481391

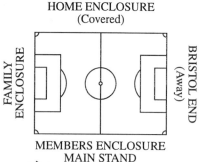

HOME ENCLOSURE
(Covered)

FAMILY ENCLOSURE

BRISTOL END (Away)

MEMBERS ENCLOSURE
MAIN STAND

Travelling Supporters Information:
Routes: Take the A36 into Bath City Centre. Follow along Pulteney Road then right into Claverton Street and along Lower Bristol Road (A36). Left under railway (1.5 miles) into Twerton High Street and ground on left.

BROMSGROVE ROVERS FC

Founded: 1885
Former Name(s): None
Nickname: 'The Rovers'
Ground: Victoria Ground, Birmingham Road, Bromsgrove, Worcs
Record Attendance: 7,563 (1957/58)

Colours: Shirts - Green & White Stripes
Shorts - Black
Telephone No.: (01527) 876949
Daytime Phone No.: (01527) 876949
Pitch Size: 110 × 72yds
Ground Capacity: 4,893
Seating Capacity: 394

GENERAL INFORMATION
Supporters Club Administrator: Chris Fox
Address: c/o Club
Telephone Number: (01527) 876949
Car Parking: At Ground (200 cars)
Coach Parking: By Police Direction
Nearest Railway Station: Bromsgrove (1.5 miles)
Nearest Bus Station: 500 yards
Club Shop: Yes
Opening Times: Weekdays 9.00am - 1.00pm and also all home matches
Telephone No.: (01527) 876949
Postal Sales: Yes
Nearest Police Station: Bromsgrove Central
Police Force: West Mercia
Police Telephone No.: (01527) 579888

GROUND INFORMATION
Away Supporters' Entrances: -
Away Supporters' Sections: Segregation not usual
Family Facilities: Location of Stand: No special facilities
Capacity of Stand: 394

ADMISSION INFO (1995/96 PRICES)
Adult Standing: £5.00
Adult Seating: £6.00
Child Standing: £1.00 (under 14's)
Child Seating: £2.00 (under 14's)
OAP Standing: £3.00
OAP Seating: £4.00
Programme Price: £1.20
FAX Number: (01527) 876949

SEATED STAND

TOWN END TERRACE

NORTH STAND

A38 BIRMINGHAM - WORCESTER ROAD

Travelling Supporters Information:
Routes: From the North: Exit the M42 at junction 1 and follow the A38 towards Bromsgrove. Once in Bromsgrove, at the traffic lights follow Town Centre signs. Victoria Ground is approximately 2 minutes away next to Clark's Motor Services on the right hand side; From the South: Exit the M5 at junction 4 onto the A38. Then as above.

DAGENHAM & REDBRIDGE FC

Founded: 1992
Former Name(s): Formed by merging of Dagenham FC & Redbridge Forest FC
Nickname: 'The Daggers' / 'The Reds'
Ground: Victoria Road, Dagenham, Essex, RM10 7XL
Record Attendance: 7,100 (1967)

Colours: Shirts - Red
  Shorts - Red with Blue Trim
Telephone No.: (0181) 592-1549
Office Phone No.: (0181) 592-7194
Daytime Phone No.: (0181) 593-7070
Pitch Size: 112 × 72yds
Ground Capacity: 5,500
Seating Capacity: 720

GENERAL INFORMATION
Supporters Club Administrator: Richard White
Address: -
Telephone Number: (01268) 418564
Car Parking: Car Park at Ground
Coach Parking: Car Park at Ground
Nearest Railway Station: Dagenham East (5 minutes walk)
Nearest Bus Station: Romford
Club Shop: At Ground
Opening Times: Matchdays Only
Telephone No.: (0181) 592-7194
Postal Sales: Yes
Nearest Police Station: Dagenham East
Police Force: Metropolitan
Police Telephone No.: (0181) 593-8232

GROUND INFORMATION
Away Supporters' Entrances: Pondfield Road
Away Supporters' Sections: Pondfield End
Family Facilities: Location of Stand: No special facilities
Capacity of Stand: -

ADMISSION INFO (1995/96 PRICES)
Adult Standing: £5.00
Adult Seating: £7.00
Child Standing: £4.00
Child Seating: £7.00
Programme Price: £1.20
FAX Number: (0181) 593-7227

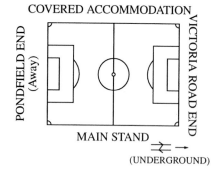

Travelling Supporters Information:
Routes: From West: Take A118 or A12 (Eastern Avenue) into Dagenham turning right into Whalebone Lane. Branch left at Sports Arena into Wood Lane, then Rainham Road. After 0.5 mile turn right into Victoria Road for Ground; From East: Take A118 or A12 (Eastern Avenue) into Dagenham turning left into Whalebone Lane (then as West); From North: Take B174 from Romford straight into Whalebone Lane (then as West from Eastern Avenue).

DOVER ATHLETIC FC

Founded: 1983
Former Name(s): None
Nickname: 'Lillywhites'
Ground: Crabble Athletic Ground, Lewisham Road, River, Dover, Kent
Record Attendance: 4,035

Colours: Shirts - White
          Shorts - Black
Telephone No.: (01304) 822373
Daytime Phone No.: (01304) 822373
Pitch Size: 110 × 75yds
Ground Capacity: 6,500
Seating Capacity: 1,000

GENERAL INFORMATION
Supporters Club Administrator: Chris Graves
Address: Dover Athletic Supporters Club, 4 Albert Road, Canterbury, Kent
Telephone Number: (01227) 769708
Car Parking: Street Parking
Coach Parking: Street Parking
Nearest Railway Station: Kearsney (1 mile)
Nearest Bus Station: Pencester Road, Dover (1.5 miles)
Club Shop: Yes
Opening Times: Matchdays Only
Telephone No.: (01304) 240041
Postal Sales: Yes
Nearest Police Station: Dover
Police Force: Kent County Constabulary
Police Telephone No.: (01304) 240055

GROUND INFORMATION
Away Supporters' Entrances: No Segregation
Away Supporters' Sections: -
Family Facilities: Location of Stand: No special facilities
Capacity of Stand: -

ADMISSION INFO (1995/96 PRICES)
Adult Standing: £5.50
Adult Seating: £6.50
Child Standing: £2.50
Child Seating: £3.00
Programme Price: £1.20
FAX Number: (01304) 210273

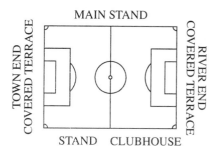

Travelling Supporters Information:
Routes: By A2 to Whitfield roundabout. Take 4th exit down hill to mini-roundabout - turn left - go 1 mile to traffic lights on hill. Turn sharp right, under railway bridge - ground is on left a further 300 yards.

FARNBOROUGH TOWN FC

Founded: 1967
Former Name(s): None
Nickname: 'The Boro'
Ground: John Roberts Ground, Cherrywood Road, Farnborough
Record Attendance: 3,069 (1992)

Colours: Shirts - Yellow with Blue Sleeves
Shorts - Blue
Telephone No.: (01252) 541469
Daytime Phone No.: (01252) 541469
Pitch Size: 115 × 77yds
Ground Capacity: 4,900
Seating Capacity: 500

GENERAL INFORMATION

Supporters Club Administrator: Mark Hardy
Address: 118 Christchurch Drive, Blackwater Camberley, Surrey   GU17 0HN
Telephone Number: (01276) 35820
Car Parking: Car Park at Ground
Coach Parking: At Ground
Nearest Railway Station: Farnborough (Main), Farnborough North & Frimley
Nearest Bus Station: -
Club Shop: Yes
Opening Times: Matchdays Only
Telephone No.: -
Postal Sales: Via Club
Nearest Police Station: Farnborough
Police Force: Hampshire
Police Telephone No.: (01252) 24545

GROUND INFORMATION

Away Supporters' Entrances: Moor Road
Away Supporters' Sections: Moor Road End

DISABLED SUPPORTERS INFORMATION
Wheelchairs: Accommodated
Disabled Toilets: None
The Blind: No Special Facilities

ADMISSION INFO (1995/96 PRICES)
Adult Standing: £5.00
Adult Seating: £6.00
Child Standing: £3.00
Child Seating: £4.00
Programme Price: £1.00
FAX Number: (01252) 546387

COVERED TERRACES

MOOR ROAD END

PROSPECT ROAD END

MAIN STAND

Travelling Supporters Information:
Routes: Exit M3 junction 4 heading for Frimley. At Roundabout take A331 towards Farnborough. At Traffic Lights, turn right into Prospect Avenue and then take 2nd right into Cherrywood Road for the Ground.

GATESHEAD FC

Founded: 1930 (Reformed 1977)	**Colours**: Shirts - Black & White Halves
Former Name(s): Gateshead United	Shorts - Black
Nickname: 'Tynesiders'	**Telephone No.**: (0191) 478-3883
Ground: International Stadium, Neilson Road,	**Daytime Phone No.**: (0191) 478-3883
Gateshead NE10 0EF	**Pitch Size**: 110 × 70yds
Record Attendance: 5,012 (20/8/84)	**Ground Capacity**: 11,750
	Seating Capacity: 11,750

GENERAL INFORMATION
Supporters Club Administrator:
Tommy Doleman
Address: 3 Frazer Terrace, Gateshead, Tyne
& Wear   NE10 0YA
Telephone Number: (0191) 469-2688
Car Parking: At Stadium
Coach Parking: At Stadium
Nearest Railway Station: Gateshead Stadium
Metro (0.5 mile); Newcastle (B.R.) 1.5 miles
Nearest Bus Station: Gateshead Interchange
(1 mile)
Club Shop: Yes - At Stadium
Opening Times: Matchdays Only
Telephone No.: (0191) 478-3883
Postal Sales: Yes
Nearest Police Station: Gateshead
Police Force: Northumbria
Police Telephone No.: (0191) 232-3451

GROUND INFORMATION
Away Supporters' Entrances: None Specified
Away Supporters' Sections: None Specified
Family Facilities: Location of Stand:
None specified
Capacity of Stand: 3,300

ADMISSION INFO (1995/96 PRICES)
Adult Seating: £5.00
Child Seating: £3.00
Programme Price: £1.00
FAX Number: (0191) 477-1315

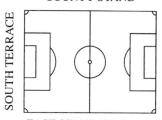

TYNE & WEAR
COUNTY STAND

SOUTH TERRACE

NORTH TERRACE

EAST STAND TERRACE

Travelling Supporters Information:
Routes: Take A1(M) to end of Motorway, just north of Washington (Birtley Services). Fork right (A194M)
to the end then turn left at the roundabout on to the A184. The stadium is 3 miles on the right.

HALIFAX TOWN FC

Founded: 1911	**Record Attendance**: 36,885 (14/2/53)
Turned Professional: 1911	**Colours**: Shirts - Blue
Limited Company: 1911	Shorts - White
Admitted to League: 1921	**Telephone No.**: (01422) 345543
Former Name(s): None	**Daytime Phone No.**: (01422) 345543
Nickname: 'Shaymen'	**Pitch Size**: 110 × 75yds
Ground: Shay Ground, Shay Syke, Halifax	**Ground Capacity**: 8,049
HX1 2YS	**Seating Capacity**: 1,896

GENERAL INFORMATION
Supporters Club Administrator: Secretary, Stephen Kell
Address: Halifax Town Promotions, 18 Prescott Street, Halifax
Telephone Number: (01422) 353423
Car Parking: Shaw Hill Car Park (Nearby)
Coach Parking: Calderdale Bus Depot (Shaw Hill)
Nearest Railway Station: Halifax (3 minutes walk)
Nearest Bus Station: Halifax (10 mins. walk)
Club Shop: Prescott Street, Halifax
Opening Times: Weekdays 9.30am - 5.00pm (Except Thursdays) & Matchdays
Telephone No.: (01422) 353423
Postal Sales: Yes
Nearest Police Station: Halifax (0.25 mile)
Police Force: West Yorkshire
Police Telephone No.: (01422) 360333

GROUND INFORMATION
Away Supporters' Entrances: Shay Syke turnstiles
Away Supporters' Sections: Visitor's enclosure, Shay Syke
Family Facilities: Location of Stand: None specified
Capacity of Stand: -

ADMISSION INFO (1995/96 PRICES)
Adult Standing: £6.00
Adult Seating: £7.00
Child Standing: £3.00
Child Seating: £3.50
Programme Price: £1.20
FAX Number: (01422) 349487

Huddersfield Road (A629)
(Away) MAIN STAND

OPEN TERRACE (Away)

HUNGER HILL

FAMILY & DISABLED STAND

Travelling Supporters Information:
Routes: From North: Take A629 to Halifax Town Centre. Take 2nd exit at roundabout into Broad Street and follow signs for Huddersfield (A629) into Skircoat Road; From South, East & West: Exit M62 junction 24 and follow Halifax (A629) signs to Town Centre into Skircoat Road for Ground.

HEDNESFORD TOWN FC

Founded: 1880
Former Name(s): Club formed by amalgamation of West Hill & Hill Top in 1880
Nickname: 'The Pitmen'
Ground: Cross Keys Ground, Hill Street, Hednesford
Record Attendance: 10,000 (1919-1920)

Colours: Shirts - White & Black Halves
Shorts - Black
Telephone No.: (01543) 422870
Daytime Phone No.: (01543) 422870
Pitch Size: 114 × 70yds
Ground Capacity: 5,000
Seating Capacity: 500

GENERAL INFORMATION
Supporters Club Administrator: Phil Lloyd
Address: c/o Club
Telephone Number: (01543) 422870
Car Parking: Space for 200 cars at ground
Coach Parking: Available at ground
Nearest Railway Station: Hednesford (0.5m)
Nearest Bus Station: Hednesford
Club Shop: Yes
Opening Times: Home matches only
Telephone No.: (01543) 422870
Postal Sales: Yes
Nearest Police Station: Hednesford
Police Force: Staffordshire
Police Telephone No.: (01543) 574545

GROUND INFORMATION
Away Supporters' Entrances: No Segregation
Away Supporters' Sections: No Segregation
Family Facilities: Location of Stand:
Lower Road End & Heath Hayes End
Capacity of Stand: 500

ADMISSION INFO (1995/96 PRICES)
Adult Standing: £5.00
Adult Seating: £6.00
Child Standing: £3.00
Child Seating: £4.00
Programme Price: £1.20
FAX Number: (01543) 428180

HEATH HAYES

TOP END

BOTTOM END

LOWER ROAD

Travelling Supporters Information:
Routes: Exit M6 at junction 11 to Cannock and follow A460 towards Hednesford. After 2 miles turn right opposite the Shell Garage, ground is at bottom of hill on right.

KETTERING TOWN FC

Founded: 1872	**Colours**: Shirts - Red
Former Name(s): None	Shorts - Red
Nickname: 'The Poppies'	**Telephone No.**: (01536) 83028/410815
Ground: Rockingham Road, Kettering,	**Daytime Phone No.**: (01536) 83028
Northants	**Pitch Size**: 110 × 70yds
Record Attendance: 11,526 (1947-48)	**Ground Capacity**: 6,500
	Seating Capacity: 1,800

GENERAL INFORMATION
Supporters Trust Administrator: c/o Club
Address: -
Telephone Number: -
Car Parking: At Ground
Coach Parking: Cattle Market, Northfield Avenue, Kettering
Nearest Railway Station: Kettering (1 mile)
Nearest Bus Station: Kettering (1 mile)
Club Shop: At Ground. Also at Chalkleys in Silver Street, Kettering
Opening Times: Shop hours in Town Centre, Matchdays and on request at the Ground
Telephone No.: (01536) 83028
Postal Sales: Yes
Nearest Police Station: London Road, Kettering
Police Force: Northants
Police Telephone No.: (01536) 411411

GROUND INFORMATION
Away Supporters' Entrances: Rockingham Road
Away Supporters' Sections: Rockingham Road End
Family Facilities: Location of Stand:
None specified
Capacity of Stand: -

ADMISSION INFO (1995/96 PRICES)
Adult Standing: £5.00
Adult Seating: £7.00
Child Standing: £4.00
Child Seating: £5.00
Programme Price: £1.20
FAX Number: (01536) 412273

Travelling Supporters Information:
Routes: To reach Kettering from the A1, M1 or M6, use the A14. The Ground is situated to the North of Kettering (1 mile) on the main A6003 Rockingham Road (to Oakham).

KIDDERMINSTER HARRIERS FC

Founded: 1886
Former Name(s): None
Nickname: 'Harriers'
Ground: Aggborough, Hoo Road, Kidderminster, Worcestershire
Record Attendance: 9,155 (1948)

Colours: Shirts - Red & White Halves
Shorts - Red
Telephone No.: (01562) 823931
Pitch Size: 112 × 72yds
Ground Capacity: 6,200
Seating Capacity: 1,100

GENERAL INFORMATION
Supporters Club Administrator: R. Thomas
Address: Kidderminster Harriers Social & Supporters Club, Stadium Close, Kidderminster
Telephone Number: (01562) 740198
Car Parking: At Ground
Coach Parking: At Ground
Nearest Railway Station: Kidderminster
Nearest Bus Station: Kidderminster Town Centre
Club Shop: Yes
Opening Times: Weekdays 9.00am - 5.00pm & First Team Matchdays
Telephone No.: (01562) 823931
Postal Sales: Yes
Nearest Police Station: Habberley Road, Kidderminster
Police Force: West Mercia
Police Telephone No.: (01562) 820888

GROUND INFORMATION
Away Supporters' Entrances: South Entrance
Away Supporters' Sections: South Stand
Family Facilities: Location of Stand:
No special facilities
Capacity of Stand: -

ADMISSION INFO (1995/96 PRICES)
Adult Standing: £5.00
Adult Seating: £6.00
Child Standing: £3.00
Child Seating: £4.00
Programme Price: £1.20
FAX Number: (01562) 827329
Junior Supporters Under 14's Club-Members:
£7.00 per season
Under 16's: £20.00 per season

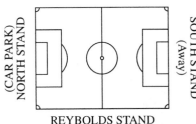

BILL GREAVES STAND

(CAR PARK)
NORTH STAND

(CAR PARK)
SOUTH STAND
(Away)

REYBOLDS STAND
(HOO ROAD)

Travelling Supporters Information:
Routes: From North: Exit M5 (junction 3) and take A456 to Kidderminster. Turn left at the traffic lights (A449 Worcester) then through the next set of traffic lights and under the railway viaduct to the traffic island. Turn right round the island and take 1st left 100 yards into Hoo Road; From South: Exit M5 (junction 6) and take A449 to Kidderminster. Turn right at the first traffic island approaching the town centre. Take 1st left into Hoo Road; Alternative Route: Exit M42 at junction 1 and take A38 to Bromsgrove and A448 to Kidderminster. At the first traffic island on town approach turn left into Spennells Valley Road. Straight on at the next traffic island, under the railway viaduct, then as North.

MACCLESFIELD TOWN FC

Founded: 1875	**Colours**: Shirts - Blue
Former Name(s): Macclesfield FC	Shorts - White
Nickname: 'The Silkmen'	**Telephone No.**: (01625) 424324/511113
Ground: Moss Rose Ground, London Road,	**Daytime Phone No.**: (01625) 511545
Macclesfield, Cheshire	**Pitch Size**: 110 × 72yds
Record Attendance: 10,041 (1948)	**Ground Capacity**: 6,000
	Seating Capacity: 1,000

GENERAL INFORMATION
Supporters Club Administrator:
Carole Wood
Address: 178 Warwick Road, Macclesfield
Telephone Number: (01625) 617670
Car Parking: Ample near Ground
Coach Parking: Near Ground
Nearest Railway Station: Macclesfield
(1 mile)
Nearest Bus Station: Macclesfield
Club Shop:
Opening Times: Matchdays 2.00 - 5.00pm
Telephone No.: (01625) 511545
Postal Sales: Yes
Nearest Police Station: Macclesfield
Police Force: Cheshire
Police Telephone No.: (01625) 610000

GROUND INFORMATION
Away Supporters' Entrances: Moss Lane
Away Supporters' Sections: Star Lane
Family Facilities: Location of Stand:
Not specified
Capacity of Stand: -

ADMISSION INFO (1995/96 PRICES)
Adult Standing: £5.00
Adult Seating: £6.00
Child Standing: £3.00
Child Seating: £4.00
Programme Price: £1.00
FAX Number: (01625) 619021

FAMILY ENCLOSURE

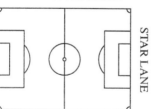

Travelling Supporters Information:
Routes: From the North: Exit M6 at junction 19 to Knutsford, follow the A537 to Macclesfield. Follow signs for the town centre, then for A523 to Leek. The Ground is 1 mile out of the town centre on the right; From the South: Exit M6 at junction 17 for Sandbach and follow the A534 to Congleton. Then take the A536 to Macclesfield. After passing The Rising Sun on the left, 0.25 mile on turn right after the Texaco Garage (Moss Lane). Following this lane will bring you to the back of the ground.

MORECAMBE FC

Founded: 1920
Former Name(s): Woodhill Lane (1920)
Nickname: 'Shrimps'
Ground: Christie Park, Lancaster Road, Morecambe LA4 4TJ
Record Attendance: 10,000 (13/1/62)

Colours: Shirts - Red and Black
Shorts - White
Telephone No.: (01524) 411797
Daytime Phone No.: (01524) 411797
Pitch Size: 118 × 76yds
Ground Capacity: 4,500
Seating Capacity: 1,000

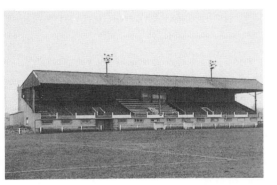

GENERAL INFORMATION
Supporters Club Administrator:
-
Address: -
Telephone Number: -
Car Parking: At Ground
Coach Parking: At Ground
Nearest Railway Station: Morecambe Central (0.5 mile)
Nearest Bus Station: Morecambe
Club Shop: Yes
Opening Times: Matchdays and by arrangement
Telephone No.: (01524) 411797 or 833358
Postal Sales: Yes
Nearest Police Station: Morecambe
Police Force: Lancashire
Police Telephone No.: (01524) 411534

GROUND INFORMATION
Away Supporters' Entrances: Corner of South Terrace and Lancaster Road
Away Supporters' Sections: South Terrace
Family Facilities: Location of Stand:
None specified
Capacity of Stand: -

ADMISSION INFO (1995/96 PRICES)
Adult Standing: £5.00
Adult Seating: £5.50
Child Standing: £3.50
Child Seating: £4.00
Programme Price: £1.20
FAX Number: (01524) 411797

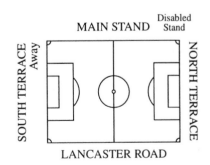

Travelling Supporters Information:
Routes: Exit M6 at junction 34. Then take A683 west in Lancaster and pick-up the A589 to Morecambe. At second roundabout on the outskirts of Morecambe, take 2nd exit into Lancaster Road and ground is on left, approximately 800 yards.

NORTHWICH VICTORIA FC

Founded: 1874	**Colours**: Shirts - Green
Former Name(s): None	Shorts - White
Nickname: 'The Vics'	**Telephone No.**: (01606) 41450
Ground: The Drill Field, Field Road,	**Daytime Phone No.**: (01606) 41450
Northwich, Cheshire	**Pitch Size**: 110 × 73yds
Record Attendance: 11,290 (1949)	**Ground Capacity**: Currently 3,600
	Seating Capacity: 660

GENERAL INFORMATION
Supporters Club Administrator:
Dave Caldwell
Address: c/o Club
Telephone Number: (01606) 75964
Car Parking: Street Parking
Coach Parking: Old Fire Station - adjacent
Nearest Railway Station: Northwich (1.5 miles)
Nearest Bus Station: 100 yards
Club Shop: At ground
Opening Times: Matchdays Only
Telephone No.: (01606) 41450
Postal Sales: Yes
Nearest Police Station: Chester Way, Northwich
Police Force: Cheshire
Police Telephone No.: (01606) 48000

GROUND INFORMATION
Away Supporters' Entrances: Terminus End
Away Supporters' Sections: Terminus End
Family Facilities: Location of Stand:
Not specified
Capacity of Stand: -
ADMISSION INFO (1995/96 PRICES)
Adult Standing: £5.00
Adult Seating: £6.00
Child Standing: £2.00
Child Seating: £4.00
Programme Price: £1.20
FAX Number: (01606) 330577

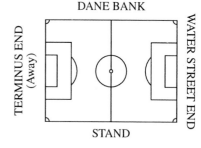

Travelling Supporters Information:
Routes: From North & South: Exit M6 junction 19 and take A556. Turn right at second roundabout (A559) and follow road for 1.5 miles - ground on right; From East & West: Take A556 to junction with A559, then as North.

RUNCORN FC

Founded: 1919
Former Name(s): None
Nickname: 'The Linnets'
Ground: Canal Street, Runcorn, Cheshire
Record Attendance: 10,111

Colours: Shirts - Yellow
Shorts - Green
Telephone No.: (01928) 575858 (Social Club)
Daytime Phone No.: (01928) 560076
Pitch Size: 110 × 70yds
Ground Capacity: 4,500
Seating Capacity: 449

GENERAL INFORMATION
Supporters Club Administrator: Noel Bell
Address: c/o Club
Telephone Number: (01928) 560076
Car Parking: At Ground
Coach Parking: At Ground
Nearest Railway Station: Runcorn (1 mile)
Nearest Bus Station: Runcorn Old Town (1 mile)
Club Shop: Yes
Opening Times: Matchdays Only
Telephone No.: None
Postal Sales: Yes
Nearest Police Station: Shopping City, Runcorn
Police Force: Cheshire
Police Telephone No.: (01928) 713456

GROUND INFORMATION
Away Supporters' Entrances: River End
Away Supporters' Sections: River End
Family Facilities: Location of Stand:
Not specified
Capacity of Stand: -

ADMISSION INFO (1995/96 PRICES)
Adult Standing: £5.00
Adult Seating: £6.00
Child Standing: £2.50
Child Seating: £3.00
Programme Price: £1.20
FAX Number: (01928) 560076

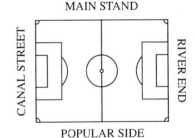

MAIN STAND

CANAL STREET

RIVER END

POPULAR SIDE

Travelling Supporters Information:
Routes: Exit M56 junction 11 and follow signs for Runcorn Old Town.
Or: Exit M62 at junction 7 and take the road to Widnes (following signs for Runcorn & Widnes Bridge).
Cross over bridge and follow signs for Runcorn Old Town then take 2nd exit for ground.

SLOUGH TOWN FC

Founded: 1890	**Colours**: Shirts - Amber
Limited Company: February 1992	Shorts - Navy Blue
Former Name(s): Slough, Slough United	**Telephone No.**: (01753) 523358
Nickname: 'The Rebels'	**Daytime Phone No.**: (01753) 523358
Ground: Wexham Park Stadium, Wexham	**Pitch Size**: 110 × 70yds
Road, Slough SL2 5QR	**Ground Capacity**: 5,000
Record Attendance: 5,000 (1982)	**Seating Capacity**: 450

GENERAL INFORMATION
Supporters Association Administrator: Chris Sliski
Address: 143 Knolton Way, Slough
Telephone Number: (01753) 526891
Car Parking: Spaces for 460 cars at Ground
Coach Parking: 3 coach bays at Ground
Nearest Railway Station: Slough (2 miles)
Nearest Bus Station: Slough (2 miles)
Club Shop: Yes - Under the Stand
Opening Times: Daily
Telephone No.: (01753) 523358
Postal Sales: Yes
Nearest Police Station: Slough
Police Force: Thames Valley
Police Telephone No.: (01753) 506000

GROUND INFORMATION
Away Supporters' Entrances: North End to right of Clubhouse (Normally No Segregation)
Away Supporters' Sections: Golf Driving Range End /North End
Family Facilities: Location of Stand: None specified
Capacity of Stand: 390

ADMISSION INFO (1995/96 PRICES)
Adult Standing: £6.00
Adult Seating: £7.50
Child Standing: £3.00   **Programme**: £1.20
Child Seating: £4.50   **Fax**: (01753) 516956

CLUBHOUSE
(MAIN STAND)

GOLF RANGE
NORTH END
(Away)

TOWN END

WEST SIDE

Travelling Supporters Information:
Routes: From North: Take the M25 to junction 16 and join M40. Exit at junction 1, Follow A412 (South) through Iver Heath to George Green. At the 2nd set of traffic lights turn right by the George Public House in George Green. Church Lane is 1 mile to the end, then turn left at the small roundabout and the ground is 0.25 mile on the right; From East: Take the M25 to junction 15 and join M4. Exit at junction 5 and follow A4 westbound as far as the Co-op Superstore on the right. Join A412 Northbound towards Uxbridge and follow the dual carriageway to the 4th set of traffic lights. Enter Church Lane, then as North; From South: (from Windsor Direction) Take A355 then onto the M4 and exit at junction 6 onto the A4. Turn right, pass Brunel Bus Station on left, Tesco Superstore, also on the left then turn first left into Wexham Road, signposted Wexham Park Hospital. Ground is just over 1 mile on the left; From West: Take M4 to junction 6 then follow route from South.

SOUTHPORT FC

Founded: 1881
Former Name(s): Southport Vulcan FC;
Southport Central FC
Nickname: 'The Sand Grounders'
Ground: Haig Avenue, Southport, Merseyside
Record Attendance: 20,010 (1936)

Colours: Shirts - Old Gold
    Shorts - Black
Telephone No.: (01704) 533422
Daytime Phone No.: (01704) 211428
Pitch Size: 115 × 78yds
Ground Capacity: 6,500
Seating Capacity: 1,880

GENERAL INFORMATION
Supporters Club Administrator:
Roy Morris
Address: 'Manikata', 3 Stretton Drive,
Southport
Telephone Number: (01704) 211428
Car Parking: Street Parking
Coach Parking: Adjacent to Ground
Nearest Railway Station: Southport (1.5 miles)
Nearest Bus Station: Town Centre
Club Shop: Yes
Opening Times: Matchdays 2.30pm (or 7.00pm) & also at Half-time. Fridays 7-9pm
Telephone No.: (01704) 533422
Postal Sales: Yes
Nearest Police Station: Southport
Police Force: Merseyside
Police Telephone No.: (0151) 709-6010

GROUND INFORMATION
Away Supporters' Entrances: Blowick End
Away Supporters' Sections: Blowick End Terrace
Family Facilities: Location of Stand:
None specified
Capacity of Stand: -
ADMISSION INFO (1995/96 PRICES)
Adult Standing: £5.00
Adult Seating: £6.00
Child Standing: £2.50
Child Seating: £3.00
Programme Price: £1.20
FAX Number: (0151) 448-1982

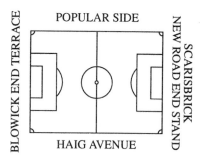

POPULAR SIDE

BLOWICK END TERRACE

NEW ROAD END STAND

SCARISBRICK

HAIG AVENUE

Travelling Supporters Information:
Routes: Exit M58 at junction 2 and take the A570 to Southport. At the first roundabout turn left into Scarisbrick New Road, pass over brook and turn right into Haig Avenue. Ground is on the right.

STALYBRIDGE CELTIC FC

Founded: 1909
Former Name(s): None
Nickname: 'Celtic'
Ground: Bower Fold, Mottram Road, Stalybridge, Cheshire
Record Attendance: 13,500

Colours: Shirts - Blue & White Quarters
Shorts - Blue
Telephone No.: (0161) 338-2828
Daytime Phone No.: (0161) 338-2828
Pitch Size: 120 × 72yds
Ground Capacity: 6,000
Seating Capacity: 1,000

GENERAL INFORMATION
Supporters Club Administrator: John Hall
Address: 44 Chunal Lane, Glossop, Derbyshire SK13 9JX
Telephone Number: (01457) 869262
Car Parking: At Ground
Coach Parking: At Ground
Nearest Railway Station: Stalybridge (1 ml)
Nearest Bus Station: Stalybridge town centre
Club Shop: Yes
Opening Times: Monday-Friday & Saturday Matchdays 10.00am - 5.00pm
Telephone No.: (0161) 338-2828
Postal Sales: Yes
Nearest Police Station: Stalybridge Town Centre
Police Force: Greater Manchester
Police Telephone No.: (0161) 330-8321

GROUND INFORMATION
Away Supporters' Entrances: Mottram End (though not normally segregated)
Away Supporters' Sections: Mottram End
Family Facilities: Location of Stand: Popular Side
Capacity of Stand: 100

ADMISSION INFO (1995/96 PRICES)
Adult Standing: £5.00
Adult Seating: £6.00
Child Standing: £3.00
Child Seating: £4.00
Programme Price: £1.20
FAX Number: (0161) 338-8256

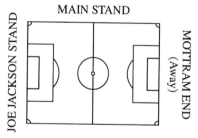

Travelling Supporters Information:
Routes: From the North: Take the M62 and exit at junction 19. Follow signs for Ashton-under-Lyne and then Stalybridge. Ground is approximately 1 mile through the town on the A6107 Mottram Road. From the Midlands and South: Take the M6, M56 and M67, leaving at the end of the motorway. Go across the roundabout to the traffic lights and turn left. The ground is approximately 2 miles on the left before the Hare & Hounds pub.

STEVENAGE BOROUGH FC

Founded: 1976
Former Name(s): None
Nickname: 'Boro'
Ground: Stevenage Stadium, Broadhall Way, Stevenage, Herts SG2 8RH
Record Attendance: 3,005 v Harrow (May 94)

Colours: Shirts - Red & White Stripes
Shorts - White
Telephone No.: (01438) 743322
Daytime Phone No.: (01438) 743322
Pitch Size: 110 × 70yds
Ground Capacity: 3,700
Seating Capacity: 472

GENERAL INFORMATION
Supporters Club Administrator: Mervyn Stoke Geddis
Address: 21 Woodland Way, Stevenage
Telephone Number: (01438) 313236
Car Parking: Spaces for 150 cars at ground and Fairlands Show Ground (opposite)
Coach Parking: At Ground
Nearest Railway Station: Stevenage (1 mile)
Nearest Bus Station: Stevenage
Club Shop: Yes
Opening Times: Matchdays Only
Telephone No.: (01438) 743322
Postal Sales: None
Nearest Police Station: Stevenage
Police Force: Hertfordshire
Police Telephone No.: (01438) 757000

GROUND INFORMATION
Away Supporters' Entrances: No Segregation
Away Supporters' Sections: No Segregation
Family Facilities: Location of Stand:
-
Capacity of Stand: 472

ADMISSION INFO (1995/96 PRICES)
Adult Standing: £5.00
Adult Seating: £7.00
Child Standing: £3.00
Child Seating: £4.00
Programme Price: £1.20
FAX Number: (01438) 743666

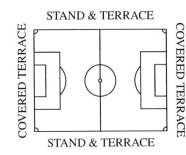

Travelling Supporters Information:
Routes: Exit A1(M) at junction 7 and take B197. Ground is on right at second roundabout.
Bus Routes: SB4 & SB5

TELFORD UNITED FC

Founded: 1877
Former Name(s): Wellington Town FC
Nickname: 'Lillywhites'
Ground: Bucks Head Ground, Watling Street, Wellington, Telford, Shropshire
Record Attendance: 13,000 (1935)

Colours: Shirts - White
    Shorts - Blue
Telephone No.: (01952) 223838
Daytime Phone No.: (01952) 223838
Pitch Size: 110 × 73yds
Ground Capacity: 4,600
Seating Capacity: 1,222

GENERAL INFORMATION
Supporters Club Administrator: The Secretary
Address: c/o Club
Telephone Number: (01952) 255662
Car Parking: At Ground
Coach Parking: At Ground
Nearest Railway Station: Wellington - Telford West
Nearest Bus Station: -
Club Shop: Yes
Opening Times: Matchdays Only
Telephone No.: (01952) 223838
Postal Sales: Yes
Nearest Police Station: Wellington
Police Force: West Mercia
Police Telephone No.: (01952) 290888

GROUND INFORMATION
Away Supporters' Entrances: North Bank Turnstiles
Away Supporters' Sections: North Bank
Family Facilities: Location of Stand: None specified
Capacity of Stand: -

ADMISSION INFO (1995/96 PRICES)
Adult Standing: £5.00
Adult Seating: £7.00
Child Standing: £3.00
Child Seating: £4.00 & £5.00
Programme Price: £1.20
FAX Number: (01952) 246431

BLOCKLEYS STAND

NORTH BANK (Away)

WATLING STREET

WEST STAND

Travelling Supporters Information:
Routes: Exit M54 junction 6 and take A518 and B5061 to Wellington district of town. Ground is on B5061 - formerly the main A5.

WELLING UNITED FC

Founded: 1963	**Colours**: Shirts - Red with White facings
Former Name(s): None	Shorts - Red
Nickname: 'The Wings'	**Telephone No.**: (0181) 301-1196
Ground: Park View Road Ground, Welling, Kent	**Daytime Phone No.**: (0181) 301-1196
	Pitch Size: 112 × 72yds
Record Attendance: 4,020 (1989/90)	**Ground Capacity**: 5,500
	Seating Capacity: 500

GENERAL INFORMATION
Supporters Club Administrator: G. Youens
Address: c/o Club
Telephone Number: -
Car Parking: Street Parking Only
Coach Parking: Outside Ground
Nearest Railway Station: Welling (0.75 ml)
Nearest Bus Station: Bexleyheath
Club Shop: Yes
Opening Times: Matchdays Only
Telephone No.: (0181) 301-1196
Postal Sales: Yes
Nearest Police Station: Welling (0.5 mile)
Police Force: Metropolitan
Police Telephone No.: (0181) 304-3161

GROUND INFORMATION
Away Supporters' Entrances: -
Away Supporters' Sections: Danson Park End
Family Facilities: Location of Stand:
None specified
Capacity of Stand: -

ADMISSION INFO (1995/96 PRICES)
Adult Standing: £5.00
Adult Seating: £6.00
Child Standing: £2.50
Child Seating: £3.50
Programme Price: £1.20
FAX Number: (0181) 301-5676

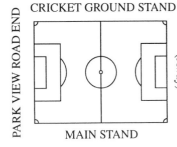

Travelling Supporters Information:
Routes: Take A2 (Rochester Way) from London, then A221 Northwards (Danson Road) to Bexleyheath. At end turn left towards Welling along Park View Road. Ground on left.

WOKING FC

Founded: 1889	**Colours**: Shirts - Red & White Halves
Former Name(s): None	Shorts - Black
Nickname: 'Cardinals'	**Telephone No.**: (01483) 772470
Ground: Kingfield Sports Ground, Kingsfield	**Daytime Phone No.**: (01483) 772470
Road, Woking, Surrey GU22 9AA	**Pitch Size**: 113 × 70yds
Record Attendance: 6,000	**Ground Capacity**: 6,000
	Seating Capacity: 500

GENERAL INFORMATION
Supporters Club Administrator: Secretary, Mr. A. Barnes
Address: c/o Club
Telephone Number: (01483) 772470
Car Parking: Spaces for 150 cars at Ground
Coach Parking: At or opposite Ground
Nearest Railway Station: Woking (1 mile)
Nearest Bus Station: Woking
Club Shop: Yes
Opening Times: All Week & Matchdays
Telephone No.: (01483) 772470
Postal Sales: Yes
Nearest Police Station: Woking
Police Force: Surrey
Police Telephone No.: (01483) 761991

GROUND INFORMATION
Away Supporters' Entrances: Kingfield Road or Westfield Avenue (if segregation in force)
Family Facilities: Location of Stand:
-
Capacity of Stand: 500
ADMISSION INFO (1995/96 PRICES)
Adult Standing: £5.00
Adult Seating: £6.20
Child/OAP Standing: £3.00
Child/OAP Seating: £4.20
Programme Price: £1.20
FAX Number: (01483) 776126

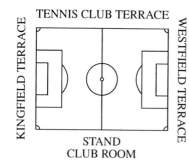

TENNIS CLUB TERRACE

KINGFIELD TERRACE

WESTFIELD TERRACE

STAND
CLUB ROOM

Travelling Supporters Information:
Routes: Exit M25 junction 10 and follow A30 towards Guildford, leave at next junction on B2215 through Ripley to join A247 to Woking OR Exit M25 junction 11 and follow A320 to Woking Town Centre, Ground on outskirts - follow signs on A320 then A247.

AYLESBURY UNITED FC

Founded: 1897
Former Name(s): None
Nickname: 'The Ducks'
Ground: The Stadium, Buckingham Road, Aylesbury, Bucks
Record Attendance: 6,031

Colours: Shirts - Green
　　　　　 Shorts - Green
Telephone No.: (01296) 436350
Daytime Phone No.: (01296) 436350
Pitch Size: 112 × 74yds
Ground Capacity: 4,878
Seating Capacity: 400

GENERAL INFORMATION
Supporters Club Administrator:
The Secretary
Address: c/o Club
Telephone Number: (01296) 436891
Car Parking: 250 Cars at Ground
Coach Parking: At Ground
Nearest Railway Station: Aylesbury Town
(20 minutes walk)
Nearest Bus Station: Aylesbury Bus Station
(20 minutes walk)
Club Shop: At Ground
Opening Times: Matchdays & Office Hours
Telephone No.: (01296) 436350
Postal Sales: Yes
Nearest Police Station: Aylesbury
Police Force: Thames Valley
Police Telephone No.: (01296) 396000

GROUND INFORMATION
Away Supporters' Entrances: Country End
Away Supporters' Sections: Country End
Family Facilities: Location of Stand:
None specified
Capacity of Stand: -

ADMISSION INFO (1995-96 PRICES)
Adult Standing: £4.50
Adult Seating: £5.00
Child Standing: £2.00
Child Seating: £2.50
Programme Price: £1.00
FAX Number: (01296) 395667

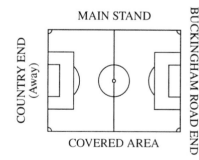

Travelling Supporters Information:
Routes: From Buckingham Direction: On outskirts of town, on left; From all other directions: Follow signs A413 Buckingham, ground on outskirts of town on right.

BISHOPS STORTFORD FC

Founded: 1874
Former Name(s): None
Nickname: 'Blues' 'Bishops'
Ground: George Wilson Stadium, Rhodes Avenue, Bishops Stortford, Herts   CM23 3JN
Record Attendance: 6,000 (1972)

Colours: Shirts - Blue & White Stripes
  Shorts - Blue
Telephone No.: (01279) 654140
Secretary: (01279) 652531
Pitch Size: 112 × 78yds
Ground Capacity: 4,500
Seating Capacity: 300

GENERAL INFORMATION
Supporters Club Administrator: John Griggs
Address: c/o Club
Telephone Number: -
Car Parking: At Ground
Coach Parking: At Ground
Nearest Railway Station: Bishop's Stortford (10 minutes walk)
Nearest Bus Station: Bishop's Stortford (10 minutes walk)
Club Shop: Yes
Opening Times: Matchdays Only
Telephone No.: (01279) 658536
Postal Sales: Yes
Nearest Police Station: Bishop's Stortford
Police Force: Hertfordshire Constabulary
Police Telephone No.: -

GROUND INFORMATION
Away Supporters' Entrances: No Segregation
Away Supporters' Sections: No Segregation
Family Facilities: Location of Stand: None specified
Capacity of Stand: -

ADMISSION INFO   (1995/96 PRICES)
Adult Standing: £4.50
Adult Seating: £5.00
Child Standing: £2.00
Child Seating: £2.50
Programme Price: £1.00
FAX Number: -

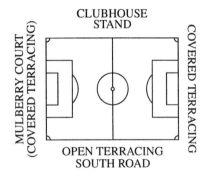

Travelling Supporters Information:
Routes: Exit M11 Junction 11 and take A120 towards town centre. Turn right at crossroads onto A1184 (London Road) then right again at mini-roundabout. Cross railway bridge then turn right at next roundabout (next to garage) and then 2nd left into Rhodes Avenue for the ground.

BOREHAM WOOD FC

Founded: 1946 **Former Name(s)**: Boreham Rovers FC and Royal Retournez FC **Nickname**: 'The Wood' **Ground**: Meadow Park, Broughinge Road, Boreham Wood, Hertfordshire **Record Attendance**: 2,500 vs St. Albans City (1971)	**Colours**: Shirts - White Shorts - Black **Telephone No.**: (0181) 953-5097 **Contact Phone No.**: (0181) 207-7982 **Pitch Size**: 112 × 72yds **Ground Capacity**: 3,500 **Seating Capacity**: 400

GENERAL INFORMATION
Supporters Club Administrator: None
Address: -
Telephone Number: -
Car Parking: At Ground
Coach Parking: At Ground
Nearest Railway Station: Elstree & Boreham Wood (0.5 mile)
Nearest Bus Station: Barnet
Club Shop: Yes
Opening Times: Matchdays Only
Telephone No.: (0181) 953-5097
Postal Sales: -
Nearest Police Station: Boreham Wood (0.25 mile)
Police Force: Metropolitan
Police Telephone No.: -

GROUND INFORMATION
Away Supporters' Entrances: No Segregation
Away Supporters' Sections: No Segregation

ADMISSION INFO (1995/96 PRICES)
Adult Standing: £4.50
Adult Seating: £5.00
Child Standing: Prices vary (Some games free)
Child Seating: Prices vary (Some games free)
Programme Price: £1.00
FAX Number: (0181) 953-5097

MAIN STAND

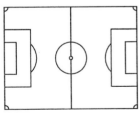

COVERED TERRACE

Travelling Supporters Information:
Routes: Exit M25 at Junction 23 and take A1 South. After 2-3 miles take Boreham Wood exit into Town. Turn right at the studio roundabout into Brook Road then next right into Broughinge Road for the Ground.

BROMLEY FC

Founded: 1892
Former Name(s): None
Nickname: 'Lilywhites'
Ground: Hayes Lane, Bromley, Kent
Record Attendance: 12,000 (24/9/49)

Colours: Shirts - White
        Shorts - Black
Telephone No.: (0181) 460-5291
Daytime Phone No.: (0181) 460-5291
Pitch Size: 112 × 78yds
Ground Capacity: 8,500
Seating Capacity: 2,000

GENERAL INFORMATION
Supporters Club Administrator:
Jack Freeman
Address: c/o Club
Telephone Number: (0181) 460-5291
Car Parking: 300 Cars at Ground
Coach Parking: At Ground
Nearest Railway Station: Bromley South
(1 mile)
Nearest Bus Station: High Street, Bromley
Club Shop: Yes
Opening Times: Matchdays Only
Telephone No.: -
Postal Sales: Yes
Nearest Police Station: Widmore Road,
Bromley
Police Force: Metropolitan 'P' Division (3
miles)
Police Telephone No.: (0181) 697-9212

GROUND INFORMATION
Away Supporters' Entrances: No Segregation
Away Supporters' Sections: No Segregation
Family Facilities: Location of Stand:
None Specified
Capacity of Stand: -

ADMISSION INFO (1995/96 PRICES)
Adult Standing: £4.50
Adult Seating: £5.00
Child Standing: £2.50
Child Seating: £2.50
Programme Price: £1.00
FAX Number: -

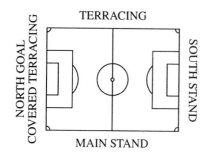

Travelling Supporters Information:
Routes: Exit M25 at A21 turnoff for Bromley and follow to A232 Croydon to Orpington Road. 1.5 miles past West Wickham (on Hayes Common), turn left into Baston Road (B265). Follow along into Hayes Street and then Hayes Lane. Ground is 0.5 mile along Hayes Lane on the right, set back from the road.

CARSHALTON ATHLETIC FC

Founded: 1905
Former Name(s): None
Nickname: 'The Robins'
Ground: War Memorial Sports Ground, Colston Avenue, Carshalton, Surrey
Record Attendance: 7,800

Colours: Shirts - Maroon with White Trim
Shorts - White
Telephone No.: (0181) 770-3692
Daytime Phone No.: (01474) 709495
Pitch Size: 117 × 76yds
Ground Capacity: 8,000
Seating Capacity: 240

GENERAL INFORMATION
Supporters Club Administrator:
Sylvia Collier
Address: c/o Club
Telephone Number: (0181) 715-2229
Car Parking: Space for 80 Cars at Ground
Coach Parking: At Ground
Nearest Railway Station: Carshalton (200 yards)
Nearest Bus Station: 400 yards
Club Shop: Yes
Opening Times: Matchdays Only
Telephone No.: -
Postal Sales: Yes
Nearest Police Station: Sutton
Police Force: Metropolitan
Police Telephone No.: (0181) 680-6212

GROUND INFORMATION
Away Supporters' Entrances: No Segregation
Away Supporters' Sections: -
Family Facilities: Location of Stand:
None specified
Capacity of Stand: -

ADMISSION INFO (1995/96 PRICES)
Adult Standing: £4.50
Adult Seating: £5.00
Child Standing: £2.50
Child Seating: £3.00
Programme Price: £1.00
FAX Number: (0181) 770-3601 (By arrangement)

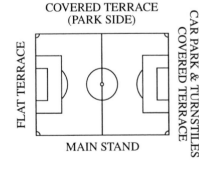

COVERED TERRACE (PARK SIDE)
FLAT TERRACE
CAR PARK & TURNSTILES COVERED TERRACE
MAIN STAND

Travelling Supporters Information:
Routes: From London: Pick up the A23 at The Elephant & Castle or The Oval. Continue along The Brixton Road (A23), through Brixton up Brixton Hill and continue past Streatham Hill to Streatham High Road (still on the A23). At the traffic lights on the junction at St.Leonard's Church, cross into Mitcham Lane (A216), continue through Streatham Road and bear left at the traffic lights at Figgs Marsh onto London Road (A217) and follow A217 through Bishopsford Road until reaching the Rose Hill roundabout. At roundabout take 1st exit into Wrythe Lane and continue for 1 mile, then turn right into Colston Avenue just before railway bridge. Ground 150 yards on right. A Private road leads to the Stadium and Car park; From the M25: Exit junction 8 on to A217 passing Lower Kingswood, Kingswood Burgh Heath, Banstead until roundabout before sign to Sutton. Bear left, still on the A217 until the Rose Hill roundabout is reached, take 4th exit then as above.

CHERTSEY TOWN FC

Founded: 1890
Former Name(s): None
Nickname: 'Curfews'
Ground: Alwyns Lane, Chertsey, Surrey
Record Attendance: 1,480 vs Walton &
                 Hersham (1963)
Colours: Shirts - Royal Blue & White Stripes
          Shorts - White

Telephone No.: (01932) 561774
Contact Address: Chris Gay, 23 Richmond
Close, Frimley, Camberley, Surrey GU16 5NR
Contact Phone No.: (01276) 20745
Pitch Size: 110 × 70yds
Ground Capacity: 3,000
Seating Capacity: 250

GENERAL INFORMATION
Supporters Club Administrator: None
Address: -
Telephone Number: -
Car Parking: Street Parking
Coach Parking: Street Parking
Nearest Railway Station: Chertsey (1 mile)
Nearest Tube Station: Chertsey (1 mile)
Club Shop: Yes
Opening Times: Matchdays Only
Telephone No.: -
Postal Sales: Yes
Nearest Police Station: Chertsey
Police Force: Surrey
Police Telephone No.: -

GROUND INFORMATION
Away Supporters' Entrances: No usual segregation
Away Supporters' Sections: No usual segregation
ADMISSION INFO (1995/96 PRICES)
Adult Standing: £4.50
Adult Seating: £5.00
Child Standing: £2.00
Child Seating: £2.50
Programme Price: £1.00
FAX Number: (01895) 621100

MAIN STAND

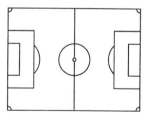

Travelling Supporters Information:
Routes: Exit M25 at junction 11 and head towards Weybridge. Turn left at the first roundabout then left at the traffic lighes into Eastworth Road. After 0.5 mile turn right at mini-roundabout into Free Prae Road then turn left at the Vine public house into London Street. Cross over the mini-roundabout and go past the Parish Chruch on the right. Pass the Swan public house and take the 1st left into Alwyns Lane for the ground.

DULWICH HAMLET FC

Founded: 1893
Former Name(s): None
Nickname: 'The Hamlet'
Ground: Champion Hill Stadium, Dog Kennel Hill, London SE22 8BD
Record Attendance: 20,744 (1933)

Colours: Shirts - Pink & Blue Stripes
Shorts - Blue
Telephone No.: (0171) 274-8707
Daytime Phone No.: (0171) 274-8707
Pitch Size: 110 × 70yds
Ground Capacity: 3,000
Seating Capacity: 500

GENERAL INFORMATION
Supporters Club Administrator:
Colin Campbell
Address: c/o Club
Telephone Number: (0171) 639-6355
Car Parking: Space for 50 cars at ground
Coach Parking: At Ground
Nearest Railway Station: East Dulwich (adjacent)
Club Shop: None
Opening Times: -
Telephone No.: -
Postal Sales: -
Nearest Police Station: East Dulwich
Police Force: Metropolitan
Police Telephone No.: (0181) 693-3366

GROUND INFORMATION
Away Supporters' Entrances: No Segregation
Away Supporters' Sections: No Segregation
Family Facilities: Location of Stand:
None specified
Capacity of Stand: -

ADMISSION INFO (1995/96 PRICES)
Adult Standing: £4.50
Adult Seating: £5.00
Child Standing: £2.50
Child Seating: £2.50
Programme Price: £1.00
FAX Number: -

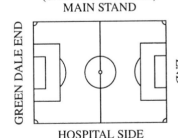

Travelling Supporters Information:
Routes: From Elephant & Castle go down Walworth Road, through Camberwell's one-way system and along Denmark Hill. Turn left by the railway into Champion Park and then right at the end down Grave Lane to the ground in Dog Kennel Hill; From the South: Come up through Streatham on the A23, turn right to Tulse Hill along the A205 (Christchurch Road) and carry on towards Sydenham. Turn left at The Grove into Lordship Lane and carry on to East Dulwich.

ENFIELD FC

Founded: 1893
Former Name(s): Enfield Spartans
Nickname: -
Ground: The Stadium, Southbury Road, Enfield, Middlesex EN1 1YQ
Record Attendance: 10,000 (10/10/62)

Colours: Shirts - White
        Shorts - Blue
Telephone No.: (0181) 292-0665
Daytime Phone No.: (0181) 292-0665
Pitch Size: 118 × 74yds
Ground Capacity: 7,200
Seating Capacity: 675

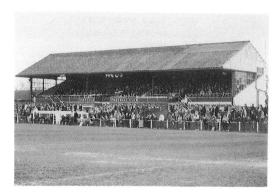

GENERAL INFORMATION
Supporters Club Administrator: Patrick Cunneen
Address: The Grumbles, Lackmore Road, Enfield, Middlesex EN1 4PB
Telephone Number: (01992) 652415
Car Parking: Adjacent to Ground
Coach Parking: Adjacent to Ground
Nearest Railway Station: Enfield Town & Southbury (both 800 yards)
Nearest Bus Station: Ponders End
Club Shop: Yes
Opening Times: Matchdays Only
Telephone No.: (0181) 292-0665
Postal Sales: Yes
Nearest Police Station: Enfield Town
Police Force: Metropolitan
Police Telephone No.: (0181) 367-2222

GROUND INFORMATION
Away Supporters' Entrances: Cambridge Road End (Only when segregated)
Away Supporters' Sections: Cambridge Road End
Family Facilities: Location of Stand: Southbury Road Side
Capacity of Stand: -

ADMISSION INFO (1995/96 PRICES)
Adult Standing: £4.50
Adult Seating: £5.50
Child Standing: £3.00
Child Seating: £5.50
Programme Price: £1.20
FAX Number: (0181) 292-0669
Note: A special Family Season Ticket is available

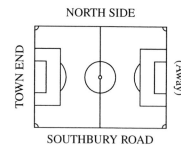

Travelling Supporters Information:
Routes: From North: Take M1 onto M25. Exit junction 25 onto A10 into Enfield; From South: Take A406 (North Circular) onto A10. Ground located at junction of A10 and A110.

GRAYS ATHLETIC FC

Founded: 1890
Former Name(s): None
Nickname: 'The Blues'
Ground: Recreation Ground, Bridge Road, Grays, Essex   RM17 6BZ
Record Attendance: 9,500 (1959)

Colours: Shirts - Royal Blue & White
Shorts - RoyalBlue
Telephone No.: (01375) 377753 (Club)
Daytime Phone No.: (01375) 391649
Pitch Size: 111 × 73yds
Ground Capacity: 5,500
Seating Capacity: 350

GENERAL INFORMATION
Supporters Club Administrator:
Bill Grove
Address: 141 Clarence Road, Grays, Essex RM17 6RD
Telephone Number: (01375) 391649
Car Parking: Car Parks close to Ground
Coach Parking: Car Parks close to Ground
Nearest Railway Station: Grays
Nearest Bus Station: Grays
Club Shop: Yes
Opening Times: Matchdays Only
Telephone No.: (01375) 377753
Postal Sales: Yes
Nearest Police Station: Grays
Police Force: Essex County Constabulary
Police Telephone No.: (01375) 391212

GROUND INFORMATION
Away Supporters' Entrances: No Segregation
Away Supporters' Sections: No Segregation
Family Facilities: Location of Stand:
None specified
Capacity of Stand: -

ADMISSION INFO (1995/96 PRICES)
Adult Standing: £4.50
Adult Seating: £4.50
Child Standing: £2.50
Child Seating: £2.50
Programme Price: £1.00
FAX Number: (01708) 851473

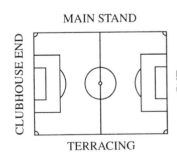

Travelling Supporters Information:
Routes: Exit M25 junctions 30-31 and take A1304. Proceed around 3 roundabouts then take 2nd right. Go straight on until Bridge Road, the Ground is on the right hand side.

HARROW BOROUGH FC

Founded: 1933
Former Name(s): Roxonians FC, Harrow Town FC
Nickname: 'The Boro'
Ground: Earlsmead, Carlyon Avenue, South Harrow, Middlesex HA2 8SS
Record Attendance: 3,000 (1946)

Colours: Shirts - Red with White Trim
 Shorts - White
Telephone No.: (0181) 422-5221 (Office)
Daytime Phone No.: (0181) 422-5221
Pitch Size: 113 × 74yds
Ground Capacity: 3,068
Seating Capacity: 250

GENERAL INFORMATION
Supporters Club Administrator: R. Snook
Address: c/o Club
Telephone Number: (0181) 422-5221
Car Parking: 90 Cars at Ground
Coach Parking: At Ground
Nearest Railway Station: Northolt Park (0.5 mile)
Nearest Tube Station: South Harrow LRT
Club Shop: Yes
Opening Times: Open every day with normal licensing hours
Telephone No.: (0181) 422-5221
Postal Sales: via Club
Nearest Police Station: South Harrow
Police Force: Metropolitan
Police Telephone No.: (0181) 900-7212

GROUND INFORMATION
Away Supporters' Entrances: Earlsmead
Away Supporters' Sections: Earlsmead
Family Facilities: Location of Stand: Arundel Stand
Capacity of Stand: 250
ADMISSION INFO (1995/96 PRICES)
Adult Standing: £4.50
Adult Seating: £4.50
Child Standing: £2.50
Child Seating: £2.50
Programme Price: £1.20
FAX Number: (0181) 422-5221

ARUNDEL DRIVE

CARLYON AVENUE

WALTON AVENUE

EARLSMEAD

Travelling Supporters Information:
Routes: Exit M25 to M40 East, carry on to A40. Turn off at the Target PH Northolt and travel past Northolt LRT station to Traffic Lights. Turn left to roundabout (near Eastcote Arms) then right into Eastcote Lane and right into Carlyon Avenue then finally right again into Earlsmead.

HAYES FC

Founded: 1909
Former Name(s): Botwell Mission
Nickname: 'The Missioners'
Ground: Church Road, Hayes, Middlesex
Record Attendance: 15,370 (10/2/51)

Colours: Shirts - Red & White Stripes
Shorts - Black
Telephone No.: (0181) 573-1932
Daytime Phone No.: (0181) 573-5342
Pitch Size: 117 × 70yds
Ground Capacity: 6,500
Seating Capacity: 450

GENERAL INFORMATION
Supporters Club Administrator:
Lee Hermitage
Address: c/o Hayes FC, Church Road
Telephone Number: (081) 573-4598
Car Parking: 300 Cars at Ground
Coach Parking: By arrangement
Nearest Railway Station: Hayes & Harlington (1 mile)
Nearest Bus Station: Hayes
Club Shop: Yes
Opening Times: 2.00pm - 5.00pm Saturday matches; 6.45 - 9.30pm Midweek matches
Telephone No.: (0181) 573-5342
Postal Sales: Address to Lee Hermitage c/o Hayes FC
Nearest Police Station: Hayes End (Morgans Lane)
Police Force: Metropolitan
Police Telephone No.: (0181) 900-7212

GROUND INFORMATION
Away Supporters' Entrances: No Segregation Usual
Away Supporters' Sections: but may be segregated at Church Road End.
Family Facilities: **Location of Stand**:
None specified
Capacity of Stand: -

ADMISSION INFO (1995/96 PRICES)
Adult Standing: £4.50
Adult Seating: £5.00
Child Standing: £2.50
Child Seating: £2.50
Programme Price: £1.00
FAX Number: None

COVERED STANDING

UNCOVERED | CHURCH ROAD | CAR PARK

GRANDSTAND

Travelling Supporters Information:
Routes: From A40: Approaching London, take Ruislip junction - turn right onto B455 Ruislip Road to White Hart Roundabout. Take Hayes by-pass to Uxbridge Road (A4020), turn right, then Church Road is 0.75 mile on the left, opposite Adam & Eve Pub. From M4: Exit junction 3 and take A312 to Parkway towards Southall, then Hayes by-pass to Uxbridge Road (A4020). Turn left, then as above.

HENDON FC

Founded: 1908
Former Name(s): Christchurch Hampstead FC
(1908-1909); Hampstead Town FC (1909-26);
Hampstead FC (1926-1933); Golders Green
FC (1933-1946)
Nickname: 'Dons' 'Greens'
Ground: Claremont Road, Cricklewood,
London NW2 1AE

Record Attendance: 9,000 (1952)
Colours: Shirts - Green
    Shorts - White
Telephone No.: (0181) 201-9494
Daytime Phone No.: (0181) 201-9494
Pitch Size: 110 × 74yds
Ground Capacity: 8,000
Seating Capacity: 381

GENERAL INFORMATION
Supporters Club Administrator:
Mike Hogan
Address: c/o Hendon FC
Telephone Number: (0181) 201-9494
Car Parking: Space for 200 Cars at Ground
Coach Parking: At Ground
Nearest Railway Station: Cricklewood (0.5 mile)
Nearest Tube Station: Brent Cross (0.5 mile)
Club Shop: Yes
Opening Times: Matchdays Only
Telephone No.: -
Postal Sales: Yes
Nearest Police Station: Golders Green
Police Force: Metropolitan
Police Telephone No.: (0181) 200-2212

GROUND INFORMATION
Away Supporters' Entrances: No Segregation
Away Supporters' Sections: -
Family Facilities: Location of Stand:
None specified
Capacity of Stand: -

ADMISSION INFO (1995/96 PRICES)
Adult Standing: £4.50
Adult Seating: £5.50
Child/Concessionary Standing: £2.50
Child/Concessionary Seating: £3.00
Programme Price: £1.20
FAX Number: (0181) 905-5966
Note: Family Season Tickets are available

COVERED TERRACING

MAIN STAND
CLAREMONT ROAD

Travelling Supporters Information:
Routes: Take the M1 or North Circular Road to the southern end of the M1. At this intersection take the exit running parallel to the A406 on its eastern side (Tilling Road). Then take 2nd right past the Holiday Inn Hotel into Claremont Road and ground is on left.

HITCHIN TOWN FC

Founded: 1865
Former Name(s): Hitchin FC & Hitchin Blue Cross FC
Nickname: 'The Canaries'
Ground: Top Field, Fishponds Road, Hitchin, Herts SG5 1NU
Record Attendance: 7,878 vs Wycombe Wanderers (1956)

Colours: Shirts - Yellow
    Shorts - Green
Telephone No.: (01462) 434483/459028
Daytime Phone No.: (01462) 456003
Pitch Size: 114 × 78yds
Ground Capacity: 3,000
Seating Capacity: 400

GENERAL INFORMATION
Supporters Club Administrator: Irvin Morgan
Address: c/o Club
Telephone Number: -
Car Parking: Space for 150 cars at ground
Coach Parking: At Ground
Nearest Railway Station: Hitchin (1 mile)
Nearest Bus Station: Hitchin-Bancroft Terminus (0.5 mile)
Club Shop: Yes
Opening Times: Matchdays Only
Phone No.: (0181) 883-2188 (Irvin Morgan)
Postal Sales: Yes
Nearest Police Station: Hitchin
Police Force: Hertfordshire
Police Telephone No.: (01438) 312323

GROUND INFORMATION
Away Supporters' Entrances: No Segregation
Away Supporters' Sections: No Segregation
Family Facilities: Location of Stand: None specified
Capacity of Stand: -

ADMISSION INFO (1994/95 PRICES)
Adult Standing: £4.50
Adult Seating: £5.00
Child Standing: £2.50
Child Seating: £3.00
Programme Price: £1.00
FAX Number: c/o (0171) 287-8156

(BEDFORD ROAD)
MAIN STAND

BEDFORD ROAD END
COVERED TERRACING
FISHPONDS ROAD END

OPEN TERRACING
ICKLEFORD END

COVERED TERRACING
POPULAR SIDE

Travelling Supporters Information:
Routes: Take A1(M) to Junction 8. Turn left onto A602. At Three Moorhens Roundabout, follow A600 to Bedford, follow over the next roundabout onto the one way system, over traffic lights and turn left at the next roundabout. The ground is immediately on the left and clearly visible.
From the Station: Out of the station, turn right and follow the pathway around to the front of the DIY centre, pass the Nightingale pub and follow down to the Woolpack Roundabout. Over the first two roundabouts then turn right at the third roundabout between the garage and Victoria pub into Bunyan Road which leads into Fishponds road on passing the Bus Depot. The ground is just past the swimming pool on the right hand side.

KINGSTONIAN FC

Founded: 1885
Former Name(s): Kingston & Surbiton YMCA (1885-87); Saxons (1887-90); Kingston Wanderers (1890-93); Kingston on Thames (1893-1908); Old Kingstonians until 1919
Nickname: 'The K's'
Ground: Kingsmeadow Stadium, Kingston Road, Kingston upon Thames, Surrey KT1 3PB

Record Attendance: Unknown (5/2/55)
Colours: Shirts - Red & White
 Shorts - Black
Telephone No.: (0181) 547-3335
Daytime Phone No.: (0181) 547-3335
Pitch Size: 115 × 80yds
Ground Capacity: 6,700
Seating Capacity: 700

GENERAL INFORMATION
Supporters Club Administrator: Ron Brown
Address: c/o Club
Telephone Number: (0181) 974-8717
Car Parking: Yes
Coach Parking: Yes
Nearest Railway Station: Norbiton (1 mile)
Nearest Bus Station: Kingston
Club Shop: Yes
Opening Times: 1.00-5.00pm & 7.00-9.00pm
Telephone No.: (0181) 547-3335
Postal Sales: Yes
Nearest Police Station: New Malden
Police Force: Metropolitan
Police Telephone No.: (0181) 541-1212

GROUND INFORMATION
Away Supporters' Entrances: No Segregation
Away Supporters' Sections: No Segregation
Family Facilities: Location of Stand:
None specified
Capacity of Stand: -

ADMISSION INFO (1995/96 PRICES)
Adult Standing: £4.00
Adult Seating: £5.00
Child Standing: £2.00
Child Seating: £2.00
Programme Price: £1.00
FAX Number: (0181) 947-5713

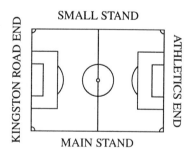

Travelling Supporters Information:
Routes: Exit M25 at junction 10 and take the A3 to the New Malden/Worcester Park turn-off and turn into Malden Road (A2043). Follow Malden Road to the mini roundabout and turn left into Kingston Road. Kingsmeadow is situated approximately 1 mile up the Kingston Road, on the left-hand side and is sign-posted from the mini-roundabout.

MOLESEY FC

Founded: 1953	**Colours**: Shirts - White
Former Name(s): None	Shorts - Black
Nickname: 'The Moles'	**Telephone No.**: (0181) 979-4823
Ground: 412 Walton Road, West Molesey,	**Daytime Phone No.**: (0181) 979-4823
Surrey KT8 0JG	**Pitch Size**: 120 × 75yds
Record Attendance: 1,255 vs Sutton United	**Ground Capacity**: 4,000
(1966)	**Seating Capacity**: 400

GENERAL INFORMATION
Supporters Club Administrator: None
Address: Social Club at Ground
Telephone Number: (0181) 979-4823
Car Parking: At Ground
Coach Parking: At Ground
Nearest Railway Station: Hampton Court (1.25 miles)
Nearest Bus Station: Lord Hotham (100yds)
Club Shop: Yes
Opening Times: Matchdays Only
Telephone No.: (0181) 979-4823
Postal Sales: Yes
Nearest Police Station: Molesey (1 mile)
Police Force: Metropolitan
Police Telephone No.: (0181) 541-1212

GROUND INFORMATION
Away Supporters' Entrances: Behind Clubhouse
Away Supporters' Sections: By Clubhouse
Family Facilities: **Location of Stand**:
None specified
Capacity of Stand: -

ADMISSION INFO (1995/96 PRICES)
Adult Standing: £4.00
Adult Seating: £4.50
Child Standing: £2.00
Child Seating: £2.30
Programme Price: £1.00
FAX Number: -

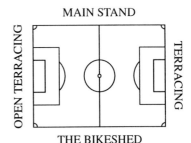

MAIN STAND

OPEN TERRACING

TERRACING

THE BIKESHED
COVERED TERRACING

Travelling Supporters Information:
Routes: Take A3 to the Hook underpass, then the A309 to the Scilly Isles roundabout and take 2nd exit into Hampton Court Way. Turn sharp left by Hampton Court Station into Bridge Road then right at next roundabout into Walton Road (B369). Ground is about 1 mile along on the left.
Alternative route: Exit M25 at junction 12 onto the M3 and proceed to Sunbury. Then follow signs 'Hampton Court' - then as above.

PURFLEET FC

Founded: 1985	**Colours**: Shirts - Yellow & Green
Former Name(s): None	Shorts - Green
Nickname: 'Fleet'	**Telephone No.**: (01708) 868901
Ground: Thurrock Hotel, Ship Lane, Grays,	**Contact No.**: (01708) 458301
Essex RM15 4HB	**Pitch Size**: 113 × 72yds
Record Attendance: 980 vs West Ham United	**Ground Capacity**: 3,500
(1989)	**Seating Capacity**: 300

GENERAL INFORMATION
Supporters Club Administrator: None
Address: -
Telephone Number: -
Car Parking: At Ground
Coach Parking: At Ground
Nearest Railway Station: Purfleet (2 miles)
Nearest Bus Station: Grays Town Centre
Club Shop: At Ground
Opening Times: Matchdays Only
Telephone No.: (01708) 868901
Postal Sales: -
Nearest Police Station: Grays
Police Force: Essex County Constabulary
Police Telephone No.: (01375) 391212

GROUND INFORMATION
Away Supporters' Entrances: No segregation
Away Supporters' Sections: -
Family Facilities: Location of Stand:
None specified
Capacity of Stand: -

ADMISSION INFO (1995/96 PRICES)
Adult Standing: £4.00
Adult Seating: £4.50
Child Standing: £2.00
Child Seating: £2.50
Programme Price: £1.00
FAX Number: (01708) 866703

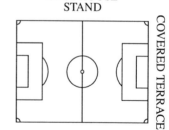

Travelling Supporters Information:
Routes: Take M25 or A13 to Dartford Tunnel roundabout - ground is then 50 yards on the right along Ship Lane.

St. Albans City fc

Founded: 1908	**Colours**: Shirts - Blue & Yellow Stripes
Former Name(s): None	Shorts - Blue
Nickname: 'The Saints'	**Telephone No.**: (01727) 866819
Ground: Clarence Park, Hatfield Road,	**Daytime Phone No.**: (01727) 864296
St. Albans, Herts	**Pitch Size**: 110 × 80yds
Record Attendance: 9,757 (27/2/26)	**Ground Capacity**: 6,000
	Seating Capacity: 900

GENERAL INFORMATION

Supporters Club Administrator:
Leigh Page
Address: 84 Ainsley Close, Edmonton,
London   N9 9SH
Telephone Number: (0181) 365-3394
Car Parking: Street Parking
Coach Parking: In Clarence Park
Nearest Railway Station: St. Albans City
(200 yards)
Nearest Bus Station: City Centre (Short
Walk)
Club Shop: Yes
Opening Times: Matchdays Only
Telephone No.: (01727) 866819
Postal Sales: Contact : Terry Edwards, 5
Wilshere Avenue, St. Albans, Herts
Nearest Police Station: Victoria Street,
St. Albans
Police Force: Hertfordshire
Police Telephone No.: (01707) 276122

GROUND INFORMATION

Away Supporters' Entrances: No Segregation
Away Supporters' Sections: -
Family Facilities: **Location of Stand**:
None specified
Capacity of Stand: -

ADMISSION INFO (1995/96 PRICES)

Adult Standing: £4.50
Adult Seating: £5.50
Child Standing: £3.00
Child Seating: £3.50
Programme Price: £1.00
FAX Number: None

MAIN STAND

HATFIELD ROAD END

YORK ROAD END

TERRACING

Travelling Supporters Information:
Routes: Take the M1 or M10 to the A405 North Orbital Road and at the roundabout at the start of the M10 go north on the A5183 (Watling Street). Turn right along St. Stephen's Hill and carry along into St. Albans. Continue up Holywell Hill go through two sets of traffic lights and at the end of St. Peter's Street take right turn at roundabout into Hatfield Road. Follow over mini-roundabouts and at second set of traffic lights turn left into Clarence Road, ground on left. Park in Clarence Road and enter ground via park or in York Road and use entrance by footbridge.

SUTTON UNITED FC

Founded: 1898
Former Name(s): Sutton Guild Rovers
Nickname: 'U's'
Ground: Borough Sports Ground, Gander Green Lane, Sutton, Surrey   SM1 2EY
Record Attendance: 14,000 (1970)

Colours: Shirts - Amber with Chocolate Trim
Shorts - Amber
Telephone No.: (0181) 644-4440
Daytime Phone No.: (0181) 644-4440
Pitch Size: 110 × 72yds
Ground Capacity: 4,652
Seating Capacity: 765

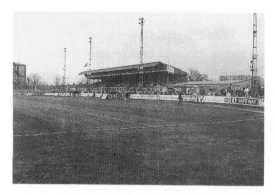

GENERAL INFORMATION
Supporters Club Administrator:
Mark Frake
Address: 165 Ridge Road, Sutton, Surrey SM3 9LW
Telephone Number: (0181) 641-2909
Car Parking: 150 Cars behind Main Stand
Coach Parking: 1 Coach in Car Park
Nearest Railway Station: West Sutton Adj.
Nearest Bus Station: -
Club Shop: Yes
Opening Times: Matchdays Only
Telephone No.: -
Postal Sales: Yes
Nearest Police Station: Sutton
Police Force: Metropolitan
Police Telephone No.: (0181) 680-6212

GROUND INFORMATION
Away Supporters' Entrances: Collingwood Road
Away Supporters' Sections: Collingwood Road Terracing
Family Facilities: Location of Stand: None specified
Capacity of Stand: -

ADMISSION INFO (1995/96 PRICES)
Adult Standing: £4.00
Adult Seating: £5.00
Child Standing: £2.00
Child Seating: £3.00
Programme Price: £1.00
FAX Number: (0181) 644-5120

```
          COVERED TERRACE
G                               C
A                               O
N  ┌─────────────────────────┐  L
D  │    ┌──┐         ┌──┐    │  L
E  │    │  │    ○    │  │    │  I
R  │    └──┘         └──┘    │  N
   │                         │  G
G  │                         │  W
R  │                         │  O
E  │    ┌──┐         ┌──┐    │  O
E  │    │  │         │  │    │  D
N  │    └──┘         └──┘    │
   └─────────────────────────┘  R
L                               O
A                               A
N                               D
E        MAIN STAND
```

Travelling Supporters Information:
Routes: Exit M25 junction 8 (Reigate Hill) and travel North on A217 for approximately 8 miles. Cross A232 then turn right at next traffic lights (Gander PH) into Gander Green Lane. Ground 300 yards on left; From London: Gander Green Lane crosses Sutton Bypass 1 mile south of Rose Hill Roundabout. Avoid Sutton Town Centre especially on Saturdays.

WALTON & HERSHAM FC

Founded: 1896
Former Name(s): None
Nickname: 'The Swans'
Ground: Stompond Lane Sports Ground, Walton-on-Thames, Surrey   KT12 1HF
Record Attendance: 6,500 vs Brighton & HA (1973/74)

Colours: Shirts - Red & White
Shorts - White
Telephone No.: (01932) 245263
Pitch Size: 110 × 70yds
Ground Capacity: 6,700
Seating Capacity: 500

GENERAL INFORMATION
Supporters Club Administrator: None
Address: -
Telephone Number: -
Car Parking: At Ground
Coach Parking: At Ground
Nearest Railway Station: Walton-on-Thames (10 minutes walk)
Nearest Bus Station: Kingston (8 miles)
Club Shop: Yes
Opening Times: Matchdays Only
Telephone No.: (01932) 244967
Postal Sales: Yes
Nearest Police Station: Walton-on-Thames
Police Force: Surrey
Police Telephone No.: -

GROUND INFORMATION
Away Supporters' Entrances: No Segregation
Away Supporters' Sections: No Segregation
Family Facilities: Location of Stand: None specified
Capacity of Stand: -

ADMISSION INFO (1995/96 PRICES)
Adult Standing: £4.50
Adult Seating: £5.00
Child Standing: £3.00
Child Seating: £3.50
Programme Price: £1.20
FAX Number: -

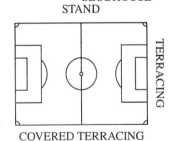

CLUBHOUSE
STAND

TERRACING

COVERED TERRACING

Travelling Supporters Information:
Routes: From the North: Pass over Walton Bridge and along New Zealand Avenue, down one-way street and up A244 (Hersham Road). Ground is then 2nd turning on the right. From Esher: Go down Lammas Lane, then Esher Road. Continue straight across first roundabout and take 4th exit at second roundabout (West Grove). Turn left at the end of Hersham Road and Stompond Land is 0.5 mile along on the left.

WORTHING FC

Founded: 1886	**Telephone No.**: (01903) 239575
Former Name(s): None	**Contact Address**: Mr. Don Read, 53 West
Nickname: 'The Rebels'	Way, Lancing, West Sussex BN15 8LX
Ground: Woodside Road, Worthing, West	**Contact Phone No.**: (01903) 751237
Sussex BN14 7QH	**Pitch Size**: 110 × 72yds
Record Attendance: Not Known	**Ground Capacity**: 4,500
Colours: Shirts - Red	**Seating Capacity**: 450
Shorts - Red	

GENERAL INFORMATION
Supporters Club Administrator: None
Address: -
Telephone Number: -
Car Parking: At Ground
Coach Parking: At Ground
Nearest Railway Station: Worthing Central (0.5 mile)
Nearest Bus Station: Worthing Central
Club Shop: Yes
Opening Times: Matchdays Only
Telephone No.: (01903) 239575
Postal Sales: Yes
Nearest Police Station: Union Place, Worthing
Police Force: West Sussex
Police Telephone No.: (01903) 231821

GROUND INFORMATION
Away Supporters' Entrances: No usual segregation
Away Supporters' Sections: No usual segregation

ADMISSION INFO (1995/96 PRICES)
Adult Standing: £4.50
Adult Seating: £4.50
Child Standing: £2.00
Child Seating: £2.50
Programme Price: £1.00
FAX Number: None

MAIN STAND

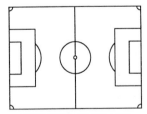

COVERED TERRACE

Travelling Supporters Information:
Routes: Take A27 or A24 to Broadwater Green Roundabout. Carry on along the main road to the end of the Green then turn right along the top of the Green past the Fire Station on the left. Take 1st exit at the next roundabout into South Farm Road. Continue along this road until approaching a level crossing then turn right into Pavilion Road. Woodside Road is then the first turn on the right.

YEADING FC

Founded: 1965	**Colours**: Shirts - Red & Black Stripes
Former Name(s): None	Shorts - Black
Nickname: 'The Ding'	**Telephone No.**: (0181) 848-7362
Ground: The Warren, Beaconsfield Road,	**Daytime Phone No.**: (0181) 848-7369
Hayes, Middlesex	**Pitch Size**: 115 × 72yds
Record Attendance: 3,000 (1990)	**Ground Capacity**: 3,500
	Seating Capacity: 250

GENERAL INFORMATION
Supporters Club Administrator:
David Lowe
Address: c/o Club
Telephone Number: (0181) 848-7369
Car Parking: Spaces for 200 cars at ground
Coach Parking: At Ground
Nearest Railway Station: Hayes (2 miles)
Nearest Bus Station: Uxbridge (2.5 miles)
Club Shop: Yes
Opening Times: Matchdays 1.30pm - 3.00pm
Weekdays 6.30pm - 7.30pm
Telephone No.: -
Postal Sales: Yes
Nearest Police Station: Uxbridge Road, Hayes
Police Force: Metropolitan
Police Telephone No.: (0181) 569-1212

GROUND INFORMATION
Away Supporters' Entrances: No Segregation
Away Supporters' Sections: No Segregation
Family Facilities: Location of Stand:
None specified
Capacity of Stand: -

ADMISSION INFO (1995/96 PRICES)
Adult Standing: £4.50
Adult Seating: £4.50
Child Standing: £2.00
Child Seating: £2.00
Programme Price: £1.00
FAX Number: (0181) 561-1063

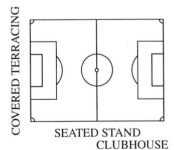

Travelling Supporters Information:
Routes: Exit M4 junction 4 and A312 past Hayes & Harlington Station. Cross the Grand Union Canal and continue to Uxbridge Road crossroad. Turn right along Uxbridge Road toward Southall about 0.75 mile and turn right at the traffic lights into Springfield Road then left into Beaconsfield Road - ground is on the right at the bottom.
Note : Do not approach from Southall end of Beaconsfield Road as there is no access because of the Grand Union Canal!

YEOVIL TOWN FC

Founded: 1923	**Colours**: Shirts - Green & White Stripes
Former Name(s): Yeovil & Petters United FC	Shorts - White
Nickname: 'Glovers'	**Telephone No.**: (01935) 23662
Ground: Huish Park, Lufton Way, Yeovil,	**Daytime Phone No.**: (01935) 23662
Somerset BA22 8YF	**Pitch Size**: 115 × 72yds
Record Attendance: 8,618	**Ground Capacity**: 8,720
	Seating Capacity: 5,212

GENERAL INFORMATION
Supporters Club Administrator: -
Address: c/o Club
Telephone Number: -
Car Parking: Car Parks for (750/1000 cars)
Coach Parking: At Ground
Nearest Railway Station: Yeovil Pen Mill (2.5 miles); Yeovil Junction (3.5 miles)
Nearest Bus Station: Yeovil (2 miles)
Club Shop: Yes
Opening Times: Monday to Friday 10.00am - 12.30pm + most evenings & Matchdays
Telephone No.: (01935) 23662
Postal Sales: Yes
Nearest Police Station: Yeovil
Police Force: Avon & Somerset
Police Telephone No.: (01935) 75291

GROUND INFORMATION
Away Supporters' Entrances: Copse Road
Away Supporters' Sections: Visitors End
Family Facilities: Location of Stand:
Blocks A & B of the Main Stand
Capacity of Stand: 600

ADMISSION INFO (1995/96 PRICES)
Adult Standing: £4.50
Adult Seating: £5.00
Child Standing: £2.50
Child Seating: £3.00
(Family Tickets are available at discounted rates)
Programme Price: £1.00
FAX Number: (01935) 73956

BARTLETT STAND

VISITORS END

HOME END

MAIN STAND

Travelling Supporters Information:
Routes: From London: Take M3 and A303 to Cartgate Roundabout. Enter Yeovil on A3088. Take 1st exit at next roundabout & straight across next roundabout into Western Avenue, turn left into Copse Road, where spectator parking is sited; From North: Exit M5 junction 25 and take A358 (Ilminster) and A303 (Eastbound) entering Yeovil on A3088, then follow directions as London.

ICIS LEAGUE DIVISION 1

ABINGDON TOWN FC
Founded: 1870 Nickname: 'The Town' Former Name: Abingdon FC. Ground: Culham Road, Abingdon OX14 3BT. Ground Capacity: 2,500 Seating Capacity: 325. Tel. No: (01235) 521684

ALDERSHOT TOWN FC
Founded: 1992 Nickname: 'The Shots' Ground: Recreation Ground, High Street, Aldershot, GU11 1TW. Ground Capacity: 5,000 Seating Capacity: 1,885. Tel. No: (01252) 20211

BARKING FC
Founded: 1880 Nickname: 'The Blues' Former Names: Barking Rovers FC, Barking Victoria FC, Barking Town FC Ground: Mayesbrook Park, Lodge Avenue, Dagenham, Essex. Ground Capacity: 4,000 Seating Capacity: 200. Tel. No: (0181) 599-2384

BARTON ROVERS FC
Founded: 1898 Nickname: 'Rovers' Ground: Sharpenhoe Road, Barton-le-Clay, Beds. MK45 4SD Ground Capacity: 4,000 Seating Capacity: 120. Tel. No: (01582) 882607; (01582) 882398 (Secretary)

BASINGSTOKE TOWN FC
Founded: 1896 Nickname: 'Stoke' Ground: Camrose Ground, Western Way, Basingstoke, Hants. Ground Capacity: 5,000 Seating Capacity: 750 Tel. No: (01256) 461465/464353 (Ground); (01734) 633105

BERKHAMSTEAD TOWN FC
Founded: 1895 Nickname: 'The Lilywhites' Former Name: Berk'stead Comrades FC. Ground: Broadwater, Lower Kings Rd, Berkhamstead, Herts HP4 2AA. Total Capacity: 2,000 Seating : 200 Tel.: (01442) 863929

BILLERICAY TOWN FC
Founded: 1880 Nickname: 'Town' 'Blues' Ground: New Lodge, Blunts Wall Road, Billericay, Essex CM12 9SA. Ground Capacity: 3,600 Seating Capacity: 236. Tel. No: (01277) 652188

BOGNOR REGIS TOWN FC
Founded: 1883 Nickname: 'The Rocks' Ground: Nyewood Lane, Bognor Regis, W.Sussex PO21 2TY Ground Capacity: 6,000 Seating: 242 Tel. No: (01243) 822325

CHESHAM UNITED FC
Founded: 1887 Nickname: 'The Generals' Ground: Meadow Park, Amy Lane, Chesham, Bucks. HP5 1NE Ground Capacity: 5,000 Seating Capacity: 250. Tel. No: (01494) 783964

HEYBRIDGE SWIFTS FC
Founded: 1882. Nickname: 'The Swifts' Former Name: Heybridge FC. Ground: Scraley Road, Heybridge, Maldon, Essex Ground Capacity: 2,500 Seating Capacity: 450. Tel.: (01621) 852978; (01621) 854798

LEYTON FC
Founded: 1868 Nickname: 'Lilywhites' Former Name: Leyton-Wingate FC. Ground: Wingate-Leyton Stadium, Lea Bridge Road, Leyton, London. Ground Capacity: 1,500 Seating Capacity: 220. Tel. No: (0181) 809-5057

MAIDENHEAD UNITED FC
Founded: 1870 Nickname: 'The Magpies' Former Names: Maidenhead FC amalgamated with Maidenhead Norfolkians FC in 1918 to form Maidenhead United FC. Ground: York Road, Maidenhead, Berks SL6 1SQ. Ground Capac.: 3,100 Seats: 300 Tel.: (01628) 36314

MARLOW FC
Founded: 1870 Nickname: 'The Blues' Former Names: Great Marlow FC. Ground: Alfred Davis Ground, Oaktree Road, Marlow, Bucks. Ground Capacity: 3,150 Seating Capacity: 260. Tel. No: (01628) 483970 (Daytime); (01628) 477032 (Infoline)

OXFORD CITY FC
Founded: 1882 Nickname: 'City' Former Names: None Ground: Court Place Farm, Marston, Oxford. Ground Capacity: 2,000 Seating Capacity: 150 Tel. No: (01865) 744493

RUISLIP MANOR FC
Founded: 1938 Nickname: 'The Manor' Ground: Grosvenor Vale, Ruislip, Middlesex. Ground Capacity: 1,500 Seating Capacity: 175. Tel. No: (01895) 637487

STAINES TOWN FC
Founded: 1892 Nickname: 'The Swans' Former Names: Staines FC, Staines Vale FC, Staines Projectile FC, Staines Lagonda FC. Ground: Wheatsheaf Park, Wheatsheaf Lane, Staines, Middlesex TW18 2PD Total Capacity: 2,500 Seating: 250 Tel.: (01784) 455988

THAME UNITED FC
Founded: 1883 Nickname: 'U's' Former Name: Thame FC, Thame Town FC. Ground: Windmill Road, Thame, Oxon. Ground Capacity: 3,000 Seating Capacity: 260. Tel. No: (01844) 213017

TOOTING & MITCHAM UNITED FC
Founded: 1932 Nickname: 'Terrors' Former Names: Tooting Town FC, Mitcham Wanderers FC. Ground: Sandy Lane, Mitcham, Surrey. Ground Capacity: 8,000 Seating Capacity: 1,900. Tel.: (0181) 646-5275 (Sec.)

UXBRIDGE FC
Founded: 1871 Nickname: 'The Reds' Ground: Honeycroft, Horton Road, West Drayton, Middlesex UB7 8HX. Ground Capacity: 4,450 Seating Capacity: 201. Tel. No: (01895) 443557

WEMBLEY FC
Founded: 1946 Nickname: 'The Lions' Ground: Vale Farm, Watford Road, Sudbury, Wembley, Middlesex HA0 4UR Ground Capacity: 4,000 Seating Capacity: 350. Tel. No: (0181) 904-8169; (0181) 908-3353 (Secretary)

WHYTELEAFE FC
Founded: 1946 Nickname: 'The Leafe' Ground: Church Road, Whyteleafe, Surrey. Ground Capacity: 5,000 Seating Capacity: 200. Tel. No: (0181) 669-1672

WOKINGHAM TOWN FC
Founded: 1875 Nickname: 'The Town' Ground: Finchamstead Road, Wokingham, Berks. Ground Capacity: 3,500 Seating Capacity: 260 Tel. No: (01734) 780243 or (01734) 780377

ICIS LEAGUE DIVISION 2

BANSTEAD ATHLETIC FC
Founded: 1944 Nickname: 'The A's' Ground: Merland Rise, Tadworth, Surrey KT20 5JG. Ground Capacity: 3,000 Seating Capacity: 250. Tel. No: (01737) 350982; (0181) 641-2957 (Secretary)

BEDFORD TOWN FC
Founded: 1908 Nickname: 'Eagles' Ground: Meadow Lane, Cardington, Bedfordshire. Ground Capacity: 3,000 Seat. Capacity: 150 Tel.: (01234) 350931 (Sec)

BRACKNELL TOWN FC
Founded: 1896 Nickname: 'The Robins' Former Names: Old Bracknell Wanderers FC, Bracknell Wednesday FC Ground: Larges Lane, Bracknell, Berks. RG12 3AN Ground Capacity: 2,500 Seating Capacity: 190. Tel. No: (01344) 412305; (01344) 300933 (Office)

CANVEY ISLAND FC
Founded: 1926 Nickname: None Ground: Park Lane, Canvey Island, Essex. Ground Capacity: 2,500 Seating Capacity: None Tel.: (01268) 682991; (01268) 698586

CHALFONT ST. PETER FC
Founded: 1926 Nickname: 'The Saints' Former Name: Gold Hill FC. Ground: The Playing Fields, Amersham Road, Chalfont St. Peter, Bucks. Ground Capacity: 2,000 Seating Capacity: 250. Tel. No: (01753) 885797

CHESHUNT FC
Founded: 1946 Nickname: 'The Ambers' Ground: The Stadium Theobalds Lane, Cheshunt, Herts. Ground Capacity: 1,500 Seating Capacity: 150 Tel. No: (01992) 626752

COLLIER ROW FC
Founded: 1929 Nickname: 'The Row' Former Names: Hampden United FC, Collier Juniors FC. Ground: Sungate, Collier Row, Romford, Essex Ground Capacity: 2,000 Seating Capacity: 120. Tel. No: (01708) 722766 (Ground), (0181) 500-9778 (Secretary)

CROYDON FC
Founded: 1953 Nickname: 'The Blues' Former Name: Croydon Amateurs FC. Ground: Croydon Sports Arena, Albert Road, South Norwood, London SE25 4QL. Ground Capacity: 8,000 Seating Capacity: 450. Tel. No: (0181) 654-8555 (Club), (0181) 654-3462 (Ground)

DORKING FC
Founded: 1880 Nickname: 'The Chicks' Former Names: Guildford Dorking Utd. FC, Dorking Town FC Ground: Meadowbank, Mill Lane, Dorking, Surrey, RH4 1DX. Ground Capacity: 3,600 Seating Capacity: 200. Tel.No: (01306) 884112; (01293) 821380 (Daytime)

EDGWARE TOWN FC
Founded: 1939 Nickname: 'Wares' Ground: White Lion Ground, High Street, Edgware, Middlesex HA8 5AQ Ground Capacity: 4,500 Seating Capacity: 300. Tel.: (0181) 952-6799 (Ground); (0181) 863-4022 (Sec)

EGHAM TOWN FC
Founded: 1896 (Reformed 1963) Nickname: 'Sarnies' Former Name: Egham FC. Ground: Tempest Road, Egham, Surrey. Ground Capacity: 3,000 Seating

Capacity: 238. Tel.: (01784) 435226; (01932) 783333

HAMPTON FC
Founded: 1920 Nickname: 'The Beavers' Ground: Beveree Stadium, Beaver Close, off Station Road, Hampton, Middlesex TW12 2BX. Ground Capacity: 2,000 Seating Capacity: 200. Tel. No: (0181) 979-2456 (Ground); (0181) 773-0858 (Secretary)

HEMEL HEMPSTEAD FC
Founded: 1885 Nickname: 'Hemel' Former Name: Apsley FC. Ground: Vauxhall Road, Adeyfield, Hemel Hempstead, Herts. Ground Capacity: 2,500 Seating Capacity: 100. Tel. No: (01442) 259777

HUNGERFORD TOWN FC
Founded: 1886 Nickname: 'The Crusaders' Ground: Town Ground, Bulpit Lane, Hungerford, Berks RG17 0AY. Ground Capacity: 3,000 Seating Capacity: 130. Tel. No: (01488) 682939/684597

LEATHERHEAD FC
Founded: 1946 Nickname: 'Tanners' Ground: Fetcham Grove, Leatherhead, Surrey KT22 9AS Ground Capacity: 3,400 Seating Capacity: 200. Tel. No: (01372) 360151

METROPOLITAN POLICE FC
Founded: 1919 Nickname: 'The Blues' Ground: Metropolitan Police (Imber Court) Sports Club, Ember Lane, Thames Ditton, Surrey Ground Capacity: 3,000 Seating Capacity: 300. Tel. No: (0181) 398-1267

NEWBURY TOWN FC
Founded: 1887 Nickname: 'The Town' Ground: Faraday Road, Newbury, Berks. Ground Capacity: 2,500 Seating Capacity: 500. Tel. No: (01635) 40048

SAFFRON WALDEN TOWN FC
Founded: 1871 Nickname: 'Bloods' Ground: Caton's Lane, Saffron Walden, Essex CB11 3AD Ground Capacity: 5,000 Seating Capacity: 400. Tel. No: (01799) 522789; (01799) 550615 (Secretary)

TILBURY FC
Founded: 1900 Nickname: 'The Dockers' Ground: Chadfields, St. Chads Road, Tilbury, Essex Ground Capacity: 3,500.Seating Capacity: 200. Tel. No: (01375) 843093

WARE FC
Founded: 1892 Nickname: 'Blues' Ground: Buryfield, Park Road, Ware, Herts SG12 0AT Ground Capacity: 4,000. Seating Capacity: 200. Tel. No: (01920) 463247; (01992) 581862 (Secretary)

WITHAM TOWN FC
Founded: 1894 (re-formed 1948) Nickname: 'The Town' Ground: Spa Road, Witham, Essex CM8 1UN Ground Capacity: 2,000 Seating Capacity: 200. Tel. No: (01376) 500146; (01376) 512990 (Secretary)

WIVENHOE TOWN FC
Founded: 1925 Nickname: 'Dragons' Ground: Broad Lane, Elmstead Road, Wivenhoe, Essex CO7 7HA. Ground Capacity: 3,000 Seating Capacity: 500. Tel.: (01206) 825380 (Ground); (01206) 825380 (Answer.)

50

ICIS LEAGUE DIVISION 3

AVELEY FC
Founded: 1927 **Nickname**: 'The Millers' **Ground**: Mill Field, Mill Road, Aveley, Essex RM15 4TR **Ground Capacity**: 8,000 **Seating Capacity**: 500. **Tel. No**: (01708) 865940; (01708) 555271 (Secretary)

CAMBERLEY TOWN FC
Founded: 1896 **Nickname**: 'Krooners' **Former Names**: Camberley FC, Yorktown FC & Camberley Wanderers FC. **Ground**: Krooner Park, Krooner Road, Camberley, Surrey, GU15 2QP. **Ground Capacity**: 2,500 **Seating Capacity**: 200. **Tel. No**: (01276) 65392 (Ground); (01276) 675221 (Secretary)

CLAPTON FC
Founded: 1878 **Nickname**: 'The Tons' **Former Names**: Downs Athletic FC **Ground**: The Old Spotted Dog Ground, Upton Lane, Forest Gate E7 9NP **Ground Capacity**: 2,000 **Seating Capacity**: 100. **Tel. No**: (0181) 472-0822; (0181) 471-3055 (Secretary)

COVE FC
Founded: 1897 **Nickname**: None **Ground**: Romayne Close, West Heath Road, Cove, Farnborough, Hants. **Ground Capacity**: 3,000 **Seating Capacity**: 100. **Tel. No**: (01252) 543615 (Ground), (01252) 518587 (Press Officer's Home)

EAST THURROCK UNITED FC
Founded: 1969 **Nickname**: 'Rocks' **Ground**: Rookery Hill, Corringham, Essex. **Ground Capacity**: 2,500. **Seating Capacity**: 160. **Tel. No**: (01375) 644166, (017082) 28818 (Secretary)

EPSOM & EWELL FC
Founded: 1917 **Nickname**: 'E's' **Former Names**: Epsom Town FC, Epsom FC. **Ground**: Merland Rise, Tadworth, Surrey KT20 5JG **Ground Capacity**: 3,000 **Seating Capacity**: 250. **Tel. No**: (01737) 350982; (01372) 729817 (Secretary) **NOTE**: Epsom & Ewell FC are currently Groundsharing with Banstead Athletic FC.

FELTHAM & HOUNSLOW BOROUGH FC
Founded: 1946 **Nickname**: 'The Borough' **Former Name**: Feltham FC. **Ground**: The Arena, Shakespeare Avenue, Feltham. **Ground Capacity**: 10,000 **Seating Capacity**: 640. **Tel. No**: (0181) 751-3663 (Sec's Home), (0181) 890-6241 (Club), (0181) 890-6119 (Ground)

FLACKWELL HEATH FC
Founded: 1907 **Nickname**: 'Heathens' **Ground**: Wilks Park, Heath End Road, Flackwell Heath, High Wycombe HP10 9EA **Ground Capacity**: 2,000 **Seating Capacity**: 150. **Tel. No**: (01628) 523892; (01628) 526204 (Sec.)

HAREFIELD UNITED FC
Founded: 1868. **Nickname**: 'The Hares'. **Ground**: Preston Park, Breakspeare Road North, Harefield, Middlesex UB9 6DG **Ground Capacity**: 2,000 **Seating Capacity**: 100 **Tel. No**: (01895) 823474

HARLOW TOWN FC
Founded: 1879 **Nickname**: 'The Hawks' **Ground**: Harlow Sportcentre, Hammarskjold Road, Harlow, Essex. **Ground Capacity**: 5,000 **Seating Capacity**: 300. **Tel. No**: (01279) 445319

HERTFORD TOWN FC
Founded: 1908 **Nickname**: 'The Blues' **Ground**: Hertingfordbury Park, West St., Hertford, Herts SG13 8EZ. **Ground Capacity**: 6,500 **Seating Capacity**: 225. **Tel.**: (01992) 583716 (Ground); (01992) 587011 (Secretary)

HORNCHURCH FC
Founded: 1923 **Nickname**: 'Urchins' **Former Names**: Upminster FC, Hornchurch & Upminster FC. **Ground**: The Stadium, Bridge Avenue, Upminster, Essex, RM14 2LX. **Ground Capacity**: 3,500 **Seating Capacity**: 300. **Tel. No**: (01708) 220080; (01708) 227891 (Secretary)

HORSHAM FC
Founded: 1885 **Nickname**: None **Ground**: Queen Street, Horsham RH13 5AD. **Ground Capacity**: 4,000 **Seating Capacity**: 300 **Tel. No**: (01403) 252310 (Ground); (01403) 264647 (Secretary)

KINGSBURY TOWN FC
Founded: 1930 **Nickname**: 'The Kings' **Ground**: Silver Jubilee Park, Townsend Lane, Kingsbury NW9 7NE **Ground Capacity**: 2,000 **Seating Capacity**: 165. **Tel. No**: (0181) 205-1645 (Ground)

LEIGHTON TOWN FC
Founded: 1885 **Nickname**: 'The Reds' **Former Name**: Leighton United FC. **Ground**: Bell Close, Lake Street, Leighton Buzzard, Beds. **Ground Capacity**: 2,360 **Seating Capacity**: 162. **Tel. No**: (01525) 373311 (Ground)

LEWES FC
Founded: 1885 **Nickname**: 'Rooks' **Ground**: The Dripping Pan, Mountfield Rd, Lewes, E.Sussex **Ground Capacity**: 5,000 **Seating Capacity**: 300. **Tel. No**: (01273) 472100; (01273) 472822 (Secretary)

NORTHWOOD FC
Founded: 1902 **Nickname**: 'The Woods' **Former Name**: Northwood Town FC **Ground**: Chestnut Avenue, Northwood, Middlesex. **Ground Capacity**: 1,750. **Seating Capacity**: 200. **Tel. No**: (01923) 827148

SOUTHALL FC
Founded: 1871 **Nickname**: None **Ground**: Western Road, Southall, Middlesex UB2 5HX **Ground Capacity**: 10,000 **Seating Capacity**: 200. **Tel.No**: (0181) 574-1084

TRING TOWN FC
Founded: 1904 **Nickname**: 'Tees' **Ground**: Pendley Sports Centre, Cow Lane, Tring, Herts **Ground Cap.**: 3,000 **Seating Capacity**: 200 **Tel. No**: (01442) 823075

WINDSOR & ETON FC
Founded: 1892 **Nickname**: 'The Royalists' **Ground**: Stag Meadow, St. Leonard's Road, Windsor, Berks SL4 3DR **Ground Capacity**: 4,500 **Seating Capacity**: 350 **Tel. No**: (01753) 860656 **Fax**: (01753) 860656

WINGATE & FINCHLEY FC
Founded: 1991 **Nickname**: None **Ground**: Bill Masters Stadium, Summers Lane, Finchley, London, N12. **Ground Capacity**: 2,000 **Seating Capacity**: 500 **Tel. No**: (0181) 446-0906

ACCRINGTON STANLEY FC

Founded: 1876 (Reformed 1968)
Former Name(s): None
Nickname: 'Stanley' 'Reds'
Ground: Crown Ground, Livingstone Road, Accrington, Lancashire
Record Attendance: 2,270 vs Gateshead
(1992/93)

Colours: Shirts - Red
Shorts - White
Telephone No.: (01254) 383235
Daytime Phone No.: (01282) 864000 (P. Terry)
Pitch Size: 112 × 72yds
Ground Capacity: 2,420
Seating Capacity: 200

GENERAL INFORMATION
Supporters Club Administrator: Tony Clements
Address: 141 Manor Street, Accrington
Telephone Number: (01254) 393996
Car Parking: 150 Cars at Ground
Coach Parking: At Ground
Nearest Railway Station: Accrington (1.5 miles)
Nearest Bus Station: Accrington Town centre
Club Shop: Yes
Opening Times: Matchdays Only
Telephone No.: (01254) 383235
Postal Sales: Yes
Nearest Police Station: Manchester Road, Accrington
Police Force: Lancashire County
Police Telephone No.: (01254) 382141

GROUND INFORMATION
Away Supporters' Entrances: Bottom Car Park
Away Supporters' Sections: Car Park Side
Family Facilities: Location of Stand:
None specified
Capacity of Stand: -
ADMISSION INFO (1995/96 PRICES)
Adult Standing: £4.00
Adult Seating: £4.00
Child Standing: £2.00
Child Seating: £2.00
Programme Price: £1.00
FAX Number: None

CAR PARK
(AWAY)

ALTHAM END

DUCKWORTH STAND

Travelling Supporters Information:
Routes: Exit M66 onto A680 to Accrington. Travel through Town Centre, then turn right into Livingstone Road.

BAMBER BRIDGE AFC

Founded: 1952
Former Name(s): None
Nickname: 'The Brig'
Ground: Irongate, Brownedge Road, Bamber Bridge, Preston, Lancashire
Record Attendance: 2,241 vs Preston (1954)
Telephone No.: (01772) 627387

Colours: Shirts - White
Shorts - White
Contact Address: John Hargreaves, 54 Selkirk Drive, Walton-le-Dale, Preston
Contact Phone No.: (01772) 39682
Pitch Size: 110 × 78yds
Ground Capacity: 3,000
Seating Capacity: 250

GENERAL INFORMATION
Supporters Club Administrator: None
Address: -
Telephone Number: -
Car Parking: At Ground
Coach Parking: At Ground
Nearest Railway Station: Bamber Bridge (1.25 miles)
Nearest Bus Station: Bamber Bridge
Club Shop: None
Opening Times: -
Telephone No.: -
Postal Sales: -
Nearest Police Station: Bamber Bridge
Police Force: Lancashire Constabulary
Police Telephone No.: -

GROUND INFORMATION
Away Supporters' Entrances: No usual segregation
Away Supporters' Sections: No usual segregation

ADMISSION INFO (1995/96 PRICES)
Adult Standing: £3.50
Child Standing: £2.00
Programme Price: £1.00
FAX Number: None

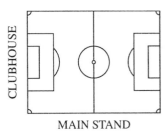

MAIN STAND

Travelling Supporters Information:
Routes: Exit M6 at junction 29 and follow Supermarket signs. Go straight through Traffic Lights and at 1st roundabout, bear right towards Preston onto London Way. The Ground is on the right as the road crosses the railway bridge and access is via the old course of Brownsedge Road, through the gates below the east side of the railway bridge.

53

BARROW AFC

Founded: 1901
Former Name(s): None
Nickname: 'Bluebirds'
Ground: Holker Street, Barrow-in-Furness, Cumbria
Record Attendance: 16,840 (1954)

Colours: Shirts - White
Shorts - Royal Blue
Telephone No.: (01229) 820346
Daytime Phone No.: (01229) 820346
Pitch Size: 110 × 75yds
Ground Capacity: 6,500
Seating Capacity: 1,000 (see Note below)

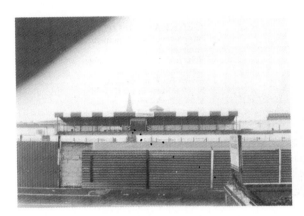

GENERAL INFORMATION
Supporters Club Administrator:
L. Barker
Address: 102 Scott Street, Barrow
Telephone Number: (01229) 823061
Car Parking: Street Parking, Popular Side Car Park and Soccer Bar Car Park
Coach Parking: Adjacent to Ground
Nearest Railway Station: Barrow Central (0.5 mile)
Nearest Bus Station: 0.5 mile
Club Shop: Yes
Opening Times: Monday to Friday 9.30am - 4.00pm
Telephone No.: (01229) 823061
Postal Sales: Yes
Nearest Police Station: Barrow
Police Force: Cumbria
Police Telephone No.: (01229) 824532

GROUND INFORMATION
Away Supporters' Entrances: -
Away Supporters' Sections: None Specified
Family Facilities: Location of Stand:
None specified
Capacity of Stand: -

ADMISSION INFO (1995/96 PRICES)
Adult Standing: £3.50
Adult Seating: £3.50
Child Standing: £2.00
Child Seating: £2.00
Programme Price: £1.00
FAX Number: (01229) 871866
Social Club: (01229) 823839
Note: No seats are available until the new stand is completed (1996).

```
                    MAIN STAND
          ┌─────────────────────────┐
   S  P   │        │        │        │  H
   M  E   │   ┌──┐ │        │ ┌──┐   │  O
   A  N   │   │  │ │   ○    │ │  │   │  L
   L      │   └──┘ │        │ └──┘   │  K  S
      O   │        │        │        │  E  T
   O  P   │        │        │        │  R  R
   P  E   │        │        │        │     E
   E  N   │        │        │        │     E
   N      └─────────────────────────┘     T
                  POPULAR END
```

Travelling Supporters Information:
Routes: Exit M6 junction 36 and take A590 through Ulverston. Turn right at the 1st roundabout on by-pass and follow signs for Barrow. After approximately 5 miles, the ground is on the left in Wilkie Road.

BISHOP AUCKLAND FC

Founded: 1886
Former Name(s): None
Nickname: 'The Bishops' 'The Blues'
Ground: Kingsway, Bishops Auckland,
Co. Durham   DL14 7JJ
Record Attendance: 17,000 (1952/53)

Colours: Shirts - Light & Dark Blue
Shorts - Navy
Telephone No.: (01388) 604403
Daytime Phone No.: (01388) 603686
Pitch Size: 111 × 71yds
Ground Capacity: 5,500
Seating Capacity: 600

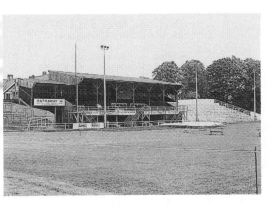

GENERAL INFORMATION
Supporters Club Administrator:
Andy Armstrong
Address: 9 Ennersdale Grove, Bishop
Auckland   DL14 9LN
Telephone Number: (01388) 835014
Car Parking: Yes at Ground
Coach Parking: In Town
Nearest Railway Station: Bishop Auckland
(0.5 mile)
Nearest Bus Station: Bishop Auckland
Club Shop: Yes
Opening Times: Matchdays Only
Telephone No.: (01388) 604403
Postal Sales: Yes
Nearest Police Station: Bishop Auckland
Police Force: County Durham
Police Telephone No.: (01388) 603566

GROUND INFORMATION
Away Supporters' Entrances: No usual segregation
Away Supporters' Sections: -
Family Facilities: **Location of Stand**:
None specified
Capacity of Stand: -
ADMISSION INFO (1995/96 PRICES)
Adult Standing: £3.50
Adult Seating: £4.00
Child Standing: £2.75
Child Seating: £3.75
Programme Price: £1.00
FAX Number: None

LIGHTFOOT   DELLWOOD
TERRACE MAIN STAND TERRACE

CLUBHOUSE TERRACE
(COVERED)

Travelling Supporters Information:
Routes: From South: A1 to Scotch Corner then follow signs to Bishop Auckland, Ground behind Town Centre; From North & West: M6 to A66 at Tebay then A66 to Barnard Castle. Follow signs to Bishop Auckland, Ground behind Town Centre.

BLYTH SPARTANS FC

Founded: 1897
Former Name(s): None
Nickname: 'Spartans'
Ground: Croft Park, Blyth, Northumberland
Record Attendance: Not Known
Colours: Shirts - Green & White Stripes
         Shorts - Green

Telephone No.: (01670) 354818
Contact Address: Bob Cotterill, 34 Folingen Estate, Blyth, Northumberland NE24 3ER
Contact Phone No.: (01670) 361057
Pitch Size: 112 × 70yds
Ground Capacity: 8,000
Seating Capacity: 600

GENERAL INFORMATION
Supporters Club Administrator: Kevin Little
Address: c/o Club
Telephone Number: (01670) 362168
Car Parking: At Ground
Coach Parking: At Ground
Nearest Railway Station: Newcastle
Nearest Bus Station: Whitley Bay (Metro)
Club Shop: Yes
Opening Times: Matchdays Only
Telephone No.: -
Postal Sales: Yes
Nearest Police Station: Blyth
Police Force: Northumbria
Police Telephone No.: -

GROUND INFORMATION
Away Supporters' Entrances: No usual segregation
Away Supporters' Sections: No usual segregation

ADMISSION INFO (1995/96 PRICES)
Adult Standing: £3.50
Adult Seating: £3.80
Child Standing: £1.75
Child Seating: £2.00
Programme Price: 80p
FAX Number: (01670) 354818

MAIN STAND

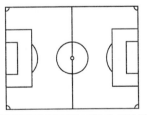

COVERED TERRACE & STAND

Travelling Supporters Information:
Routes: Pass through the Tyne Tunnel and take left lane for Morpeth (A19/A1). At the 2nd roundabout (approximately 7 miles) take full right turn for A189 (signposted Ashington). After 2 miles take slip road (A1061 signposted Blyth). Continue across 2 roundabouts and a railway crossing then turn left (A193) at next roundabout (signposted Blyth). Turn right for Quayside and ground is on left.

BOSTON UNITED FC

Founded: 1934
Former Name(s): Boston Town/Boston Swifts
Nickname: 'The Pilgrims'
Ground: York Street, Boston, Lincolnshire
Record Attendance: 10,086 vs. Corby Town

Colours: Shirts - Amber with Black Trim
    Shorts - Black
Telephone No.: (01205) 364406
Daytime Phone No.: (02105) 364406
Matchday Phone No.: (01205) 365525
Pitch Size: - 112 × 72 yds
Ground Capacity: 8,781
Seating Capacity: 1,769

GENERAL INFORMATION
Supporters Club Administrator: None
Address: -
Telephone Number: -
Car Parking: At Ground
Coach Parking: At Ground
Nearest Railway Station: Boston (0.5 miles)
Nearest Bus Station: Boston Coach Station (0.25 mile)
Club Shop: 14/16 Spain Place, Boston
Opening Times: Weekdays 9.00am - 4.30pm
Telephone No.: (01205) 364406
Postal Sales: Yes
Nearest Police Station: Boston
Police Force: Lincolnshire
Police Telephone No.: (01205) 366222

GROUND INFORMATION
Away Supporters' Entrances: Town End
Away Supporters' Sections: Town End Enclosure
Family Facilities: Location of Stand:
None specified
Capacity of Stand: -

ADMISSION INFO (1995/96 PRICES)
Adult Standing: £3.50
Adult Seating: £4.00
Child Standing: £2.50
Child Seating: £3.00
Programme Price: £1.00
FAX Number: (01205) 354063

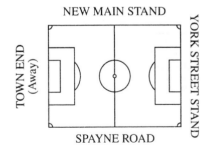

NEW MAIN STAND

TOWN END (Away)

YORK STREET STAND

SPAYNE ROAD

Travelling Supporters Information:
Routes: From North: Take A17 from Sleaford, bear right after railway crossing to traffic lights over bridge. Forward through traffic lights into York Street; From South & West: Take A16 from Spalding and turn right at traffic lights over bridge - forward through traffic lights into York Street.

BUXTON FC

Founded: 1877	**Colours**: Shirts - White
Former Name(s): None	Shorts - White
Nickname: 'The Bucks'	**Telephone No.**: (01298) 24733
Ground: The Silverlands, Buxton, Derbyshire	**Daytime Phone No.**: (01298) 24733
Record Attendance: 6,000 (1962)	**Pitch Size**: 112 × 70yds
	Ground Capacity: 4,000
	Seating Capacity: 585

GENERAL INFORMATION
Supporters Club Administrator: -
Address: -
Telephone Number: -
Car Parking: Street Parking
Coach Parking: Sylvan Park (200 yards)
Nearest Railway Station: Buxton (0.5 mile)
Nearest Bus Station: Buxton (0.25 mile)
Club Shop: Yes
Opening Times: Matchdays Only
Telephone No.: (01298) 24733
Postal Sales: Yes
Nearest Police Station: Buxton - Directly Opposite
Police Force: Derbyshire
Police Telephone No.: (01298) 72100

GROUND INFORMATION
Away Supporters' Entrances: No Segregation
Away Supporters' Sections: -
Family Facilities: Location of Stand:
None specified
Capacity of Stand: -

ADMISSION INFO (1995/96 PRICES)
Adult Standing: £3.50
Adult Seating: £3.50
Child Standing: £2.50
Child Seating: £2.50
Programme Price: 70p
FAX Number: (01298) 24733

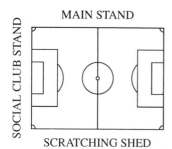

Travelling Supporters Information:
Routes: From South & East: Take A6 from Bakewell into Buxton and turn left at the traffic lights into Dale Road then right at the crossroads into the High Street. Turn third right into Hardwick Square and the ground is opposite the County Police Headquarters. From North & West: Take A6 from Stockport into Buxton, turn left at first traffic island towards Bakewell and turn right at second traffic island into Dale Road. Then as South & East.

CHORLEY FC

Founded: 1883
Former Name(s): None
Nickname: 'Magpies'
Ground: Victory Park, Duke Street, Chorley, PR7 3DU
Record Attendance: 9,679 (1931/32)

Colours: Shirts - Black & White Stripes
Shorts - Black
Telephone No.: (01257) 263406
Daytime Phone No.: (01257) 263406
Pitch Size: 112 × 72yds
Ground Capacity: 4,400
Seating Capacity: 900

GENERAL INFORMATION
Supporters Club Administrator: -
Address: -
Telephone Number: -
Car Parking: 80 Cars at Ground
Coach Parking: At Ground
Nearest Railway Station: Chorley (0.25 ml)
Nearest Bus Station: 15 mins from Ground
Club Shop: Yes
Opening Times: Matchdays Only
Telephone No.: -
Postal Sales: Yes
Nearest Police Station: St. Thomas's Road, Chorley (10 minutes)
Police Force: Lancashire Constabulary
Police Telephone No.: (01257) 262831

GROUND INFORMATION
Away Supporters' Entrances: Ashby Street & Pilling Lane Stands
Away Supporters' Sections: Pilling Lane Stand
Family Facilities: **Location of Stand**: None specified
Capacity of Stand: -

ADMISSION INFO (1995/96 PRICES)
Adult Standing: £3.50
Adult Seating: £4.50
Child Standing: £1.75
Child Seating: £2.25
Programme Price: £1.00

ASHBY STREET

TOWN END

PILLING LANE

MAIN STAND

Travelling Supporters Information:
Routes: Exit M61 junction 6 and follow A6 to Chorley. Going past the Yarrow Bridge Hotel on Bolton Road, turn left at 1st set of lights into Pilling Lane. Take 1st right into Ashby Street, Ground 2nd entrance on left. Alternative Route: Exit M6 junction 27 and follow signs to Chorley. Turn left at lights and continue down the A49 for 2.5 miles before turning right onto B5251. On entering Chorley turn right into Duke Street 200 yards past The Plough.

COLWYN BAY FC

Founded: 1885
Former Name(s): None
Nickname: 'Bay' or 'Seagulls'
Ground: Llanelian Road, Old Colwyn, Clwyd
Correspondence Address: 15 Smith Avenue,
Old Colwyn, Clwyd   LL29 8BE

Colours: Shirts - Sky Blue
　　　　　Shorts - Maroon
Telephone No.: (01492) 516941
Daytime Phone No.: (01492) 515133
Pitch Size: 110 × 75yds
Ground Capacity: 5,000
Seating Capacity: 500

GENERAL INFORMATION
Supporters Club Administrator: A. Holden
Address: Flat 2, Erskine Road, Colwyn Bay,
LL29 8EA
Telephone Number: (01492) 534287
Car Parking: At Ground
Coach Parking: At Ground
Nearest Railway Station: Colwyn Bay (1 ml)
Nearest Bus Station: Colwyn Bay
Club Shop: Yes at Ground
Opening Times: Matchdays only
Telephone No.: As for Supporters' Club
Postal Sales: Yes
Nearest Police Station: Colwyn Bay
Police Force: North Wales
Police Telephone No.: -

GROUND INFORMATION
Away Supporters' Entrances: No Segregation
Away Supporters' Sections: No Segregation
ADMISSION INFO (1995/96 PRICES)
Adult Standing: £3.50
Adult Seating: £3.50
Child Standing: £2.00
Child Seating: £2.00
Programme Price: 80p
FAX Number: None

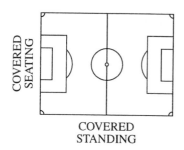

COVERED
SEATING

COVERED
STANDING

Travelling Supporters Information:
Routes: From Queensferry: Take A55 and when expressway is reached take the first exit off (signposted Old Colwyn). Turn left at the bottom of the slip road then straight on at mini roundabout into Llanelian Road. The ground is 0.5 mile on the right.

DROYLSDEN FC

Founded: 1892	**Colours**: Shirts - Red
Former Name(s): None	Shorts - Red
Nickname: 'The Bloods'	**Telephone No.**: (0161) 370-1426
Ground: Butchers Arms, Market Street,	**Daytime Phone No.**: (0161) 370-1426
Droylsden, Manchester	**Pitch Size**: 118 × 78yds
Record Attendance: 5,000	**Ground Capacity**: 3,500
	Seating Capacity: 450

GENERAL INFORMATION
Supporters Club Administrator: R Harris
Address: c/o Club
Telephone Number: -
Car Parking: 200 Cars at Ground
Coach Parking: At Ground
Nearest Railway Station: Droylsden
Nearest Bus Station: Ashton
Club Shop: Yes
Opening Times: Matchdays Only
Telephone No.: (0161) 370-1426
Postal Sales: Yes
Nearest Police Station: Manchester Road, Droylsden
Police Force: Greater Manchester
Police Telephone No.: (0161) 330-8321

GROUND INFORMATION
Away Supporters' Entrances: Greenside Lane
Away Supporters' Sections: No Segregation
Family Facilities: Location of Stand: None specified
Capacity of Stand: -

ADMISSION INFO (1995/96 PRICES)
Adult Standing: £3.50
Adult Seating: £3.50
Child Standing: £1.50
Child Seating: £1.50
Programme Price: £1.00
FAX Number: None

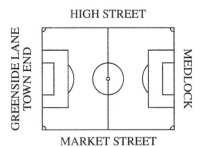

Travelling Supporters Information:
Routes: Take M62 to the end of M666 (Denton roundabout) for M56. Exit at the Denton/Ashton-under-Lyne turnoff following Droylsden signs (1-2 miles). Follow the road to the Manchester Road roundabout and along to the Traffic Lights at Market Street and turn right. Ground is 100 yards on the left.

EMLEY FC

Founded: 1903
Former Name(s): None
Nickname: None
Ground: Emley Welfare Sports Ground, Emley, Huddersfield, West Yorks.
Record Attendance: 5,134 (1/2/69)

Colours: Shirts - Sky Blue with Maroon Trim
Shorts - Maroon
Telephone No.: (01924) 848398 (Social Club)
(01924) 840087 (Matchdays Only)
Daytime Phone No.: (01484) 602720
Pitch Size: 110 × 70yds
Ground Capacity: 3,000
Seating Capacity: 220

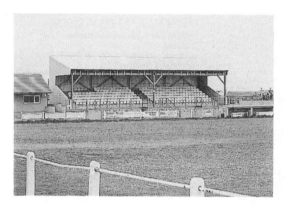

GENERAL INFORMATION
Supporters Club Administrator: None
Address: -
Telephone Number: -
Car Parking: Spaces for 150 Cars at Ground
Coach Parking: At Ground
Nearest Railway Station: Huddersfield (7 miles)
Nearest Bus Station: Huddersfield
Club Shop: Yes
Opening Times: Matchdays Only
Telephone No.: (01924) 848398
Postal Sales: Yes
Nearest Police Station: Kirkburton
Police Force: West Yorkshire
Police Telephone No.: (01484) 436897

GROUND INFORMATION
Away Supporters' Entrances: None Specified
Away Supporters' Sections: -
Family Facilities: Location of Stand:
None specified
Capacity of Stand: -

ADMISSION INFO (1995/96 PRICES)
Adult Standing: £4.00
Adult Seating: £4.50
Child Standing: £2.50
Child Seating: £3.00
Programme Price: £1.00
FAX Number: (01226) 762330

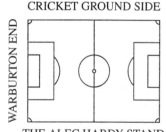

Travelling Supporters Information:
Routes: Exit M1 junction 38 and follow signs to Huddersfield. Left at Roundabout onto Denby Dale Road A636 for approximately 0.75 mile then turn right, 1 mile to Emley. From West: Exit M62 junction 23 and follow road to Huddersfield. Take Ring Road out of Huddersfield following Wakefield signs for 5 miles, through Lepton, past White Horse Public House on left, turn right at the top of the hill, Emley is 2.75 miles.

FRICKLEY ATHLETIC FC

Founded: 1910
Former Name(s): Frickley Colliery FC
Nickname: 'The Blues'
Ground: Westfield Lane, South Emsell,
Pontefract, West Yorks.
Record Attendance: 7,000 (1971)

Colours: Shirts - Blue
　　　　　Shorts - Blue & White
Telephone No.: (01977) 642460
Daytime Phone No.: (01977) 643316
Pitch Size: 117 × 78yds
Ground Capacity: 6,000
Seating Capacity: 800

GENERAL INFORMATION
Supporters Club Administrator:
H. Canner
Address: 18 Exchange Street, South Emsall,
Pontefract, West Yorks.
Telephone Number: -
Car Parking: 200 Cars at Ground
Coach Parking: At Ground
Nearest Railway Station: South Emsall (2 miles)
Nearest Bus Station: South Emsall
Club Shop: Yes
Opening Times: Matchdays Only
Telephone No.: -
Postal Sales: Yes
Nearest Police Station: South Kirkby
Police Force: West Yorkshire
Police Telephone No.: (01977) 793611

GROUND INFORMATION
Away Supporters' Entrances: No Segregation
Away Supporters' Sections: -
Family Facilities: Location of Stand:
None specified
Capacity of Stand: -

ADMISSION INFO (1995/96 PRICES)
Adult Standing: £3.50
Adult Seating: £4.00
Child Standing: £2.00
Child Seating: £2.50
Programme Price: 70p
FAX Number: None

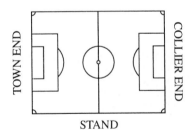

Travelling Supporters Information:
Routes: From North: Follow A1 south leave A1 at first exit after Trusthouse Forte TraveLodge and follow road to South Kirkby then onto South Emsall. Upon entering the Town Centre take Westfield Lane then Oxford Street; From South: Take M1 to M18 to A1(M) and finally onto A638. Follow road towards Wakefield then follow road to South Emsall, then as above; From West & East: Take M62 to junction with A1 and head south to first exit, then as North.

GAINSBOROUGH TRINITY FC

Founded: 1873
Former Name(s): None
Nickname: 'The Blues'
Ground: The Northolme, North Street, Gainsborough, Lincolnshire
Record Attendance: 9,760 (1948)

Colours: Shirts - Blue
        Shorts - White
Telephone No.: (01427) 613295
Daytime Phone No.: (01427) 612333
Pitch Size: 111 × 71yds
Ground Capacity: 7,500
Seating Capacity: 350

GENERAL INFORMATION
Supporters Club Administrator: M. Hewson
Address: c/o Club
Telephone Number: (01427) 613688
Car Parking: Street Parking
Coach Parking: Opposite Ground
Nearest Railway Station: Lea Road (2 miles)
Nearest Bus Station: Heaton Street (1 mile)
Club Shop: Yes
Opening Times: Matchdays Only
Telephone No.: (01427) 613295
Postal Sales: Yes
Nearest Police Station: Morton Terrace (0.5 mile)
Police Force: Lincolnshire
Police Telephone No.: (01427) 810910

GROUND INFORMATION
Away Supporters' Entrances: No Segregation
Away Supporters' Sections: -
Family Facilities: Location of Stand: None specified
Capacity of Stand: -

ADMISSION INFO (1995/96 PRICES)
Adult Standing: £4.00
Adult Seating: £4.50
Child Standing: £2.00
Child Seating: £2.50
Programme Price: £1.00
FAX Number: (01427) 615239

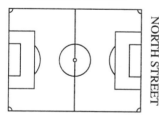

CARLISLE STREET

NORTH STREET

NORTHOLME

Travelling Supporters Information:
Routes: From North, South & West: Exit A1 near Worksop on to the A614 and take first left onto the B6420 to East Retford. Turn right on to A620 to Gainsborough and after 12 miles on outskirts of town take A631. Cross bridge, passing church and turn left along the A159. Pass Post Office and ground is 300 yards along North Street; From East: Take A631 into Gainsborough and turn left on to A159 then as North.

GUISELEY AFC

Founded: 1909	**Colours**: Shirts - White with Blue Sleeves
Former Name(s): None	Shorts - Blue
Nickname: None	**Telephone No.**: (01943) 873223
Ground: Nethermoor, Otley Road, Guiseley,	**Social Club No.**: (01943) 872872
W. Yorks.	**Pitch Size**: 110 × 69yds
Record Attendance: 2,486 v Bridlington Town	**Ground Capacity**: 3,000
(1989/90)	**Seating Capacity**: 427

GENERAL INFORMATION
Supporters Club Administrator:
Bernard Slater
Address: c/o Club
Telephone Number: -
Car Parking: At ground & Ings Crescent
Coach Parking: At Ground
Nearest Railway Station: Guiseley (5 minute walk)
Nearest Bus Station: Bus Stop outside Ground
Club Shop: Yes
Opening Times: Matchdays Only
Telephone No.: (01943) 873223
Postal Sales: Yes
Nearest Police Station: Otley
Police Force: West Yorkshire
Police Telephone No.: (01532) 585065

GROUND INFORMATION
Away Supporters' Entrances: No segregation
Away Supporters' Sections: No segregation
Family Facilities: Location of Stand:
None specified
Capacity of Stand: -

ADMISSION INFO (1995/96 PRICES)
Adult Standing: £4.00
Adult Seating: £4.00
Child Standing: £2.00
Child Seating: £2.00
Programme Price: £1.00
FAX Number: c/o (01532) 758830

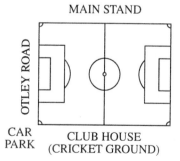

Travelling Supporters Information:
Routes: Exit M62 Junction 28 and take Leeds Road to Roundabout at Junction of A65 at Horsforth. Turn left onto A65 pass through Rawdon to Guiseley. Ground is 0.25 mile on right after traffic lights opposite Silver Cross factory.

HYDE UNITED FC

Founded: 1919
Former Name(s): Hyde FC (1885-1917)
Nickname: 'Tigers'
Ground: Tameside Stadium, Ewen Fields,
Walker Lane, Hyde, Cheshire   SK14 2SB
Record Attendance: 9,500 (1952)

Colours: Shirts - Red
    Shorts - White
Telephone No.: (0161) 368-1031 (Matchdays)
Daytime Phone No.: (0161) 368-3687
Pitch Size: 120 × 70yds
Ground Capacity: 4,000
Seating Capacity: 400

GENERAL INFORMATION
Supporters Club Administrator:
Ray Stanley
Address: 15 Balmain Avenue, Gorton,
Manchester M18
Telephone Number: (0161) 223-2445
Car Parking: 150 Cars at ground
Coach Parking: At Ground
Nearest Railway Station: Newton (0.25 ml)
Nearest Bus Station: Hyde
Club Shop: Yes
Opening Times: Matchdays Only
Telephone No.: (0161) 368-1031 or 368-3687
Postal Sales: Yes
Nearest Police Station: Hyde
Police Force: Tameside Area
Police Telephone No.: (0161) 330-8321

GROUND INFORMATION
Away Supporters' Entrances: None Specified
Away Supporters' Sections: -
Family Facilities: Location of Stand:
None specified
Capacity of Stand: -

ADMISSION INFO (1995/96 PRICES)
Adult Standing: £5.00
Adult Seating: £5.50
Child Standing: £3.00
Child Seating: £3.50
Programme Price: 70p
FAX Number: (0161) 368-3687

NEW MAIN STAND

TINKERS PASSAGE

WALKER LANE

LEIGH STREET SCHOOL

Travelling Supporters Information:
Routes: On entering Hyde follow signs for Tameside Leisure Park. When on Walker Lane, take 2nd Car
Park entrance near Leisure Pool and follow road round for Stadium.

KNOWSLEY UNITED FC

Founded: 1983	**Colours**: Shirts - Red + Black Hoops
Former Name(s): Kirkby Town FC	Shorts - Black
Nickname: 'United'	**Telephone No.**: (0151) 480-2529
Ground: Alt Park, Endmoor Road, Huyton,	**Daytime Phone**: (0151) 260-1433 (J.Williams)
Merseyside	**Pitch Size**: 112 × 75yds
Record Attendance: 951 vs Stafford Rangers	**Ground Capacity**: 9,000
(1993 F.A. Cup)	**Seating Capacity**: 300

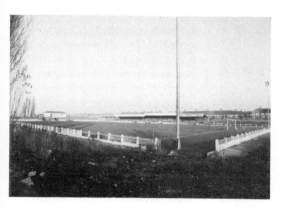

GENERAL INFORMATION
Supporters Club Administrator: None
Address: -
Telephone Number: -
Car Parking: At Ground
Coach Parking: At Ground
Nearest Railway Station: Huyton (3 miles)
Club Shop: None at Present
Opening Times: -
Telephone No.: -
Postal Sales: -
Nearest Police Station: Huyton (3 miles)
Police Force: Merseyside
Police Telephone No.: -

GROUND INFORMATION
Away Supporters' Entrances: No Segregation
Away Supporters' Sections: No Segregation
Family Facilities: Location of Stand:
None specified
Capacity of Stand: -

ADMISSION INFO (1995/96 PRICES)
Adult Standing: £3.00
Adult Seating: £3.00
Child Standing: £1.50
Child Seating: £1.50
Programme Price: 75p
FAX Number: (0151) 525-3165

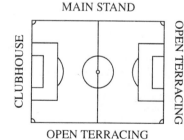

Travelling Supporters Information:
Routes: Exit M62 junction 6 and take M57 to junction 3. Follow signs for Huyton and at roundabout go straight across along Huyton Link Road. Ground is on left.

LEEK TOWN FC

Founded: 1952
Former Name(s): Abbey Green Rovers; Leek Lowe Hamil
Nickname: 'Blues'
Ground: Harrison Park, Macclesfield Road, Leek, Staffs ST13 8LD
Record Attendance: 3,048

Colours: Shirts - Blue
    Shorts - Blue
Telephone No.: (01538) 399278
Pitch Size: 115 × 80yds
Ground Capacity: 4,500
Seating Capacity: 640

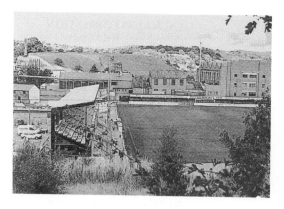

GENERAL INFORMATION
Supporters Club Administrator:
Brian Corden
Address: c/o Club
Telephone Number: (01538) 399278
Car Parking: 80 Cars at Ground
Coach Parking: At Ground
Nearest Railway Station: Stoke or Macclesfield (both 13 miles)
Nearest Bus Station: Leek
Club Shop: Yes
Opening Times: Matchdays Only
Telephone No.: (01538) 399278
Postal Sales: Yes
Nearest Police Station: Leek
Police Force: Staffordshire
Police Telephone No.: (01538) 399333

GROUND INFORMATION
Away Supporters' Entrances: Grace Street
Away Supporters' Sections: Grace Street Paddock
Family Facilities: Location of Stand:
None specified
Capacity of Stand: -

ADMISSION INFO (1995/96 PRICES)
Adult Standing: £3.50
Adult Seating: £4.00
Child Standing: £2.50
Child Seating: £3.00
Programme Price: 80p
FAX Number: (01538) 399826

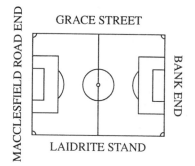

Travelling Supporters Information:
Routes: From North: Exit M6 at junction 17 to Macclesfield then follow A53 to Buxton Road; From South: Exit M6 at junction 15 to City Centre then follow A52 Leek Road. Ground is situated 0.5 mile outside Leek on Macclesfield side of the A53 Macclesfield to Buxton road.

68

MARINE FC

Founded: 1894	**Colours**: Shirts - White
Former Name(s): None	Shorts - Black
Nickname: 'Mariners' 'Lilywhites'	**Telephone No.**: (0151) 924-1743/4046
Ground: Rossett Park, College Road, Crosby,	**Daytime Phone No.**: (0151) 924-1743
Liverpool L23 3AS	**Pitch Size**: 113 × 71yds
Record Attendance: 4,000 (1949)	**Ground Capacity**: 3,000
	Seating Capacity: 400

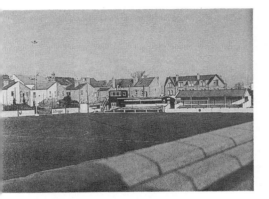

GENERAL INFORMATION
Supporters Club Administrator: Barry Lenton
Address: 16 Manor Avenue, Crosby, Liverpool L23 7YB
Telephone Number: (0151) 924-1899
Car Parking: 60 Cars at Ground
Coach Parking: -
Nearest Railway Station: Blundell Sands & Crosby (800 yards)
Nearest Bus Station: Crosby
Club Shop: Yes
Opening Times: Matchdays Only
Telephone No.: (0151) 924-4364
Postal Sales: Yes
Nearest Police Station: Crosby
Police Force: Merseyside
Police Telephone No.: (0151) 709-6010

GROUND INFORMATION
Away Supporters' Entrances: Gate A
Away Supporters' Sections: -
Family Facilities: Location of Stand: None specified
Capacity of Stand: -

ADMISSION INFO (1995/96 PRICES)
Adult Standing: £3.50
Adult Seating: £4.00
Child Standing: £2.50
Child Seating: £3.00
Programme Price: 60p
FAX Number: (0151) 236-4453

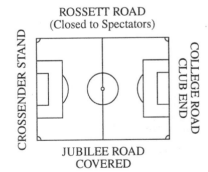

ROSSETT ROAD
(Closed to Spectators)

CROSSENDER STAND

COLLEGE ROAD CLUB END

JUBILEE ROAD
COVERED

Travelling Supporters Information:
Routes: Follow M57/M58 Motorway to end. Follow signs into Crosby Town Centre, ground is situated on College Road which is off main Liverpool-Southport A565 road. Ground is sign-posted in town.

MATLOCK TOWN FC

Founded: 1885
Former Name(s): Hall Leys (pre-1900)
Nickname: 'The Gladiators'
Ground: Causeway Lane, Matlock, Derbyshire
Record Attendance: 5,123 (1975)
Colours: Shirts - Royal Blue
        Shorts - White

Telephone No.: (01629) 55362 (Matchdays)
(01629) 583866 (24hr. Answerphone)
Daytime Phone No.: (0629) 583866
Pitch Size: 110 × 70yds
Ground Capacity: 3,200
Seating Capacity: 320

GENERAL INFORMATION
Supporters Club Administrator:
Mrs. Susan Tomlinson
Address: M.T. Aux. Association, Causeway Lane, Matlock, Derbyshire
Telephone Number: (01629) 583866
Car Parking: 46 Cars at Ground
Coach Parking: Bus Station - Town Centre
Nearest Railway Station: Matlock (500 yds)
Nearest Bus Station: 350 yards
Club Shop: Yes
Opening Times: 9.00am - 4.00pm Weekdays,
9.00am - 12.00pm Saturdays
Telephone No.: (01629) 583866
Postal Sales: Yes
Nearest Police Station: Matlock (500 yards)
Police Force: Derbyshire Constabulary
Police Telephone No.: (01629) 580100

GROUND INFORMATION
Away Supporters' Entrances: Matlock Green End
Away Supporters' Sections: Cyril Harrison Stand
Family Facilities: Location of Stand:
None specified
Capacity of Stand: -

ADMISSION INFO (1995/96 PRICES)
Adult Standing: £3.50
Adult Seating: £4.00
Child Standing: £2.00
Child Seating: £2.50
Programme Price: 70p
FAX Number: None

MAIN STAND/TERRACING

TARMAC STAND

MATLOCK GREEN END

CYRIL HARRISON STAND

Travelling Supporters Information:
Routes: Take the A6 to Matlock and at roundabout by the bus station take the A615 Alfreton Road. Causeway Lane is 500 yards along.

SPENNYMOOR UNITED FC

Founded: 1901	**Colours**: Shirts - Black & White Stripes
Former Name(s): None	Shorts - Black
Nickname: 'The Moors'	**Telephone No.**: (01388) 811934
Ground: Brewery Field, Durham Road, Spen-nymoor, Co. Durham, DL16 6JN	**Daytime Phone No.**: (01388) 814100
	Pitch Size: 113 × 70yds
Record Attendance: 7,202 v Bishop Auckland (30/3/57)	**Ground Capacity**: 5,000
	Seating Capacity: 300

GENERAL INFORMATION
Supporters Club Administrator: None
Address: -
Telephone Number: -
Car Parking: Street Parking
Coach Parking: Club will arrange
Nearest Railway Station: Durham (6 miles)
Nearest Bus Station: Durham (6 miles)
Club Shop: Yes
Opening Times: Matchdays Only
Telephone No.: -
Postal Sales: Yes
Nearest Police Station: Spennymoor
Police Force: Durham Constabulary
Police Telephone No.: (01388)

GROUND INFORMATION
Away Supporters' Entrances: No segregation
Away Supporters' Sections: No segregation
Family Facilities: Location of Stand:
None specified
Capacity of Stand: -

ADMISSION INFO (1995/96 PRICES)
Adult Standing: £3.50
Adult Seating: £4.00
Child Standing: £2.00
Child Seating: £2.50
Programme Price: £1.00
FAX Number: (01388) 811934

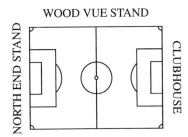

Travelling Supporters Information:
Routes: From South: Take A1(M) to A167 then A688. On entering Spennymoor go straight across mini-roundabout then take 3rd exit at next roundabout (by St. Andrew's Church). Pass Asda on left and continue straight on at junction passing Salvin Arms. Ground then 200 yards on left. From North: Take A167 to Croxdale (Ness factory) turn right at cemetery into Durham Road. Ground 0.5 mile on the right.

WINSFORD UNITED FC

Founded: 1883 **Former Name(s)**: Over Wanderers FC (prior to 1914) **Nickname**: 'Blues' **Ground**: Barton Stadium, Wharton, Winsford, Cheshire CW7 3EU **Record Attendance**: 7,000 (1947)	**Colours**: Shirts - Royal Blue Shorts - White **Telephone No.**: (01606) 593021 **Daytime Phone No.**: (01606) 861980 (Social Club) **Pitch Size**: 112 × 75yds **Ground Capacity**: 7,000 **Seating Capacity**: 600

GENERAL INFORMATION
Supporters Club Administrator: -
Address: c/o Club
Telephone Number: -
Car Parking: Space for 200 cars at ground
Coach Parking: At ground
Nearest Railway Station: Winsford (1 mile)
Nearest Bus Station: Northwich
Club Shop: Yes
Opening Times: Matchdays Only
Telephone No.: (01606) 593021
Postal Sales: Yes
Nearest Police Station: Winsford
Police Force: Cheshire
Police Telephone No.: (01606) 592222

GROUND INFORMATION
Away Supporters' Entrances: No usual segregation
Away Supporters' Sections: Big games only
Family Facilities: Location of Stand:
None specified
Capacity of Stand: -

ADMISSION INFO (1995/96 PRICES)
Adult Standing: £3.50
Adult Seating: £4.00
Child Standing: £2.50
Child Seating: £3.00
Programme Price: 80p
FAX Number: (01606) 552246

KINGSWAY

CAR PARK

WHARTON REC

WHARTON ROAD

Travelling Supporters Information:
Routes: From North: Exit M6 at junction 19 and take A556 towards Northwich and Davenham, then follow A5018 to Winsford; From South: Exit M6 at junction 18 and follow A54 through Middlewich to Winsford. Turn off main road opposite lakeside park into Wharton Road and bear left. Ground is 0.25 mile along on the right.

WITTON ALBION FC

Founded: 1890
Turned Professional: 1908
Former Name(s): -
Nickname: 'Albion'
Ground: Wincham Park, Chapel Street, Wincham, Northwich CW9 6DA
Record Attendance: 3,800

Colours: Shirts - Red & White Stripes
Shorts - Black
Telephone No.: (01606) 43008
Daytime Phone No.: (01606) 43008
Pitch Size: 115 × 75yds
Ground Capacity: 5,000
Seating Capacity: 640

GENERAL INFORMATION
Social Club Administrator:
Steve Marlor
Address: Wincham Park Social Club,
Northwich CW9 6DA
Telephone Number: (01606) 47117
Car Parking: 1,200 spaces at Ground
Coach Parking: At Ground
Nearest Railway Station: Northwich
Nearest Bus Station: Northwich
Club Shop: Yes
Opening Times: Matchdays Only
Telephone No.: (01606) 43008
Postal Sales: Yes
Nearest Police Station: Northwich
Police Force: Cheshire
Police Telephone No.: (01606) 48000

GROUND INFORMATION
Away Supporters' Entrances: Lostock End
Away Supporters' Sections: Lostock End
Family Facilities: Location of Stand:
None specified
Capacity of Stand: -

ADMISSION INFO (1995/96 PRICES)
Adult Standing: £4.00
Adult Seating: £5.00
Child Standing: £2.50
Child Seating: £3.50
Programme Price: £1.00
FAX Number: (01606) 43008

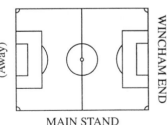

Travelling Supporters Information:
Routes: Exit M6 junction 19 and take A556 towards Northwich. After 3 miles turn right onto A559 following Warrington signs. Turn left opposite Black Greyhound Inn and ground is on left.
Alternative Route: Exit M56 junction 10 and take A559 to Black Greyhound Inn and turn right.

UNIBOND NORTHERN PREMIER - DIV. 1

ALFRETON TOWN FC
Founded: 1959 Nickname: 'Reds' Ground: The Town Ground, North Street, Alfreton, Derbyshire. Ground Capacity: 5,000 Seating Capacity: 172. Tel. No: (01773) 830277

ASHTON UNITED FC
Founded: 1878. Nickname: 'The Robins' Former Name: Hurst FC. Ground: Surrey Street, Hurst Cross, Ashton-under-Lyne, OL6 8DY Ground Capacity: 4,000 Seating Capacity: 250 Tel. No: (0161) 339-4158 (Sec.)

ATHERTON LABURNUM ROVERS FC
Founded: 1954 Nickname: 'Laburnum's' Former Name: Laburnum Rovers FC. Ground: Crilly Park, Spa Road, Atherton, Greater Manchester. Ground Capacity: 4,000 Seating Capacity: 500. Tel. No: (01942) 883950

BRADFORD PARK AVENUE FC
Founded: 1907 (Reformed 1988) Nickname: 'Avenue' Ground: McLaren Field, Town Street, Bramley, Leeds. Ground Capacity: 4,000 Seating Capacity: 1,500. Tel. No: (0113) 2564842

CONGLETON TOWN FC
Founded: 1901. Nickname: 'Bears' Former Name: Congleton Hornets FC Ground: Booth Street Ground, Crescent Road, Congleton, Cheshire. Ground Capacity: 3,000. Seating Capacity: 220. Tel. No: (01260) 274460

CURZON ASHTON FC
Founded: 1963. Nickname: 'Curzon'. Ground: 'National Park', Katherine Street, Ashton-under-Lyne, Lancs. Ground Capacity: 3,000. Seating Capacity: 350. Tel. No: (0161) 330-6033

EASTWOOD TOWN FC
Founded: 1953. Nickname: 'The Badgers' Ground: Coronation Park, Eastwood, Notts. Ground Capacity: 3,700. Seating Capacity: 200. Tel. No: (01773) 715823

FARSLEY CELTIC AFC
Founded: 1908. Nickname: 'Celts' or 'Villagers' Ground: Throstle Nest, Newlands LS28 5BE Ground Capacity: 5,500. Seating Capacity: 400. Tel. No: (0113) 2561517

FLEETWOOD FC
Founded: 1977 Nickname: 'The Fishermen' Former Names: Fleetwood Town FC Ground: Highbury Stadium, Park Avenue, Fleetwood, Lancashire. Ground Capacity: 4,500 Seating Capacity: 300. Tel. No: (01253) 771402

GREAT HARWOOD TOWN FC
Founded: 1978. Nickname: 'Arrad'. Ground: The Showground, Wood Street, Great Harwood, Lancs. Ground Capacity: 2,800. Seating Capacity: 270. Tel. No: (01254) 883913

GRETNA FC
Founded: 1946. Nickname: 'Black & Whites' Ground: Raydale Park, Dominion Road, Gretna, Carlisle Ground Capacity: 2,200. Seating Capacity: 500. Tel. No: (01461) 37602

HARROGATE TOWN FC
Founded: 1919. Nickname: 'The Sulphurites' Former Names: Harrogate FC & Harrogate Hotspurs FC. Ground: Wetherby Road, Harrogate. Ground Capacity: 3,850. Seating Capacity: 420. Tel. No: (01423) 883671

LANCASTER CITY FC
Founded: 1902 Nickname: 'Dolly Blues' Former Names: Lancaster Town FC Ground: Giant Axe, West Road, Lancaster. Ground Capacity: 5,000 Seating Capacity: 450. Tel. No: (01524) 841950; (01524) 35774

LEIGH R.M.I. FC
Founded: 1896 Nickname: 'Railwaymen' Former Names: Horwich R.M.I. FC Ground: Hilton Park, Leigh Ground Capacity: 9,240 Seating Capacity: 1,425. Tel. No: (01942) 674437 (Day); (01942) 818669 (Evening)

LINCOLN UNITED FC
Founded: 1939 Nickname: None Ground: Ashby Avenue, Hartsholme, Lincoln. Ground Capacity: 2,714. Seating Capacity: 430. Tel. No: (01522) 690674

NETHERFIELD AFC
Founded: 1920. Nickname: 'The Field'. Ground: Parkside, Parkside Road, Kendal. Ground Capacity: 4,750. Seating Capacity: 250. Tel. No: (01539) 726488

RADCLIFFE BOROUGH FC
Founded: 1949 Nickname: 'Boro' Ground: Stainton Park, Pilkington Road, Radcliffe, Manchester, M26 0PE. Ground Capacity: 3,000. Seating Capacity: 260. Tel. No: (0161) 724-5937

WARRINGTON TOWN FC
Founded: 1949. Nickname: 'Town' Former Name: Stockton Heath FC Ground: Cantilever Park, Loushers Lane, Warrington WA4 2RS Ground Capacity: 2,000 Seating Capacity: 400. Tel. No: (01925) 31932

WHITLEY BAY FC
Founded: 1950. Nickname: 'The Bay' Former Name: Whitley Bay Athletic FC. Ground: Hillheads Park, Whitley Bay, Tyne & Wear. Ground Capacity: 4,500 Seating Capacity: 300. Tel. No: (0191) 215-3680 (Ground); (0191) 252-0419 (Secretary)

WORKINGTON AFC
Founded: 1884 Nickname: 'The Reds' Ground: Borough Park, Workington, Cumbria CA14 2DT Ground Capacity: 3,000. Seating Capacity: 300. Tel. No: (01900) 605208 (Secretary)

WORKSOP FC
Founded: 1861 (Reformed 1893) Nickname: 'Tigers' Ground: Babbage Way, off Sandy Lane, Worksop. Ground Capacity: 2,500. Seating Capacity: 400. Tel. No: (01909) 501911

NORTHERN COUNTIES EAST PREMIER

ARMTHORPE WELFARE FC

Founded: 1926 (Disbanded 1974, Reformed 1976) Nickname: 'Welly' Ground: Church Street, Armthorpe, Doncaster. Ground Capacity: 2,000 Seating Capacity: 100. Tel. No: (01302) 832514

ARNOLD TOWN FC

Founded: 1989 Nickname: 'Eagles' Ground: King George V Playing Fields, Gedling Road, Arnold, Notts. Ground Capacity: 3,500 Seating Capacity: 150. Tel. No: (01602) 263660 (Ground)

ASHFIELD UNITED FC

Founded: 1885 Nickname: 'Snipes' Former Name: Sutton Town FC. Ground: Lowmoor Road, Kirkby-in-Ashfield, Notts. Ground Capacity: 8,000. Seating Capacity: 200. Tel. No: (01623) 752181

BELPER TOWN FC

Founded: 1883 Nickname: 'The Nailers' Ground: Christchurch Meadow, Bridge Street, Belper, Derbys. Ground Capacity: 4,000 Seating Capacity: 250. Tel. No: (01773) 825549

BRIGG TOWN FC

Founded: 1864 Nickname: 'The Zebras' Ground: The Hawthorns, Hawthorn Avenue, Brigg Ground Capacity: 4,000 Seating Capacity: 200. Tel. No: (01652) 652767

DENABY UNITED FC

Founded: 1895 Nickname: 'Reds' Ground: Tickhill Square, Denaby Main, Doncaster Ground Capacity: 6,000 Seating Capacity: 250. Tel. No: (01709) 864042

GLASSHOUGHTON WELFARE FC

Founded: 1964 Nickname: None Former Name: Anson Sports FC. Ground: Leeds Road, Glasshoughton, Castleford, West Yorkshire. Ground Capacity: 2,000 Seating Capacity: 100 Tel. No: (01977) 556257 (Sec.)

GOOLE TOWN FC

Founded: 1900 Nickname: 'Vikings' Ground: Victoria Pleasure Grounds, Carter Street, Goole, N. Humberside Ground Capacity: 4,500 Seating Capacity: 200 Tel. No: (01405) 762794

HALLAM FC

Founded: 1860 Nickname: 'Countrymen' Ground: Sandygate, Sandygate Road, Crosspool, Sheffield. (Sandygate is the Oldest Football Ground in the World) Ground Capacity: 2,000 Seating Capacity: 120 Tel. No: (0114) 230-9484 (Ground)

HATFIELD MAIN FC

Founded: 1936 Nickname: None Ground: Dunscroft Welfare Ground, Dunscroft, Doncaster, West Yorks. Ground Capacity: 3,000 Seating Capacity: None Tel. No: (01302) 841648

HUCKNALL TOWN FC

Founded: 1946 Nickname: 'Town' Former Name: Hucknall Colliery Welfare FC Ground: Watnall Road, Hucknall, Notts, NG15. Ground Capacity: Not known Seating Capacity: 240. Tel.: (01602) 641292 (ground)

LIVERSEDGE FC

Founded: 1910 Nickname: 'The Sedge' Ground: Clayborn Ground, Quaker Lane, Hightown Road, Cleckheaton, West Yorks Ground Capacity: 2,000 Seating Capacity: 250 Tel. No: (01274) 862108

MALTBY MINERS WELFARE FC

Founded: 1972 Nickname: 'The Miners' Former Name: 'Maltby Main' Ground: Muglet Lane, Maltby, South Yorkshire. Ground Capacity: 1,000 Seating Capacity: 200. Tel. No: (01709) 812462 (Matchdays); (01709) 815676 (Secretary)

NORTH FERRIBY UNITED FC

Founded: 1934 Nickname: 'United' Ground: Grange Lane, Church Road, North Ferriby, East Yorkshire, HU14 3AA Ground Capacity: 2,600 Seating Capacity: 240 Tel. No: (01482) 634601

OSSETT ALBION FC

Founded: 1944 Ground: Queens Terrace, Dimple Wells Road, Osset, West Yorks. Ground Capacity: 3,000 Seating Capacity: 240. Tel. No: (01924) 275630 (Sec.)

OSSETT TOWN FC

Founded: 1936 Nickname: 'The Town' Ground: 'Ingfield', Prospect Road, Ossett, Wakefield, West Yorks. Ground Capacity: 3,500 Seating Capacity: 400. Tel. No: (01226) 382415

PICKERING TOWN AFC

Founded: 1888 Nickname: 'The Pikes' Ground: Recreation Ground, Mill Lane, Pickering. Ground Capacity: 2,000 Seating Capacity: 120. Tel. No: (01751) 473348

SHEFFIELD FC

Founded: 1857 (Oldest Club in World) Nickname: 'Club' Ground: Owlerton Stadium, Sheffield Ground Capacity: 2,000 Seating Capacity: - Tel. No: (0114) 234-4553 (Secretary)

STOCKSBRIDGE PARK STEELS FC

Founded: 1959 Nickname: 'Steels' Former Name: Stocksbridge Works FC. Ground: Bracken Moor Lane, Stocksbridge, Sheffield. Ground Capacity: 1,650 Seating Capacity: 500. Tel. No: (0114) 288-2045

THACKLEY FC

Founded: 1930 Nickname: None Former Name: Thackley Wesleyians FC Ground: Dennyfield, Ainsbury Avenue, Thackley, Bradford. Ground Capacity: 4,500 Seating Capacity: 200. Tel. No: (01274) 615571

NORTHERN LEAGUE DIVISION 1

BEDLINGTON TERRIERS FC
Founded: 1949 Nickname: 'The Terriers' Ground: Welfare Park, Park Road, Bedlington, Northumberland. Ground Capacity: 2,500 Seating Capacity: 50 Tel. No: (01670) 829196 (Secretary); (01670) 825485 (Ground)

BILLINGHAM SYNTHONIA FC
Founded: 1923 Nickname: 'Synners' Ground: The Stadium, Central Avenue, Billingham, Cleveland. Ground Capacity: 1,925 Seating Capacity: 370. Tel. No: (01642) 532348 (Press Box)

CHESTER-LE-STREET TOWN FC
Founded: 1972 Nickname: 'The Cestrians' Former Name: Chester-le-Street, Garden Farm FC. Ground: Points North, Chester Moor, Chester-le-Street, County Durham DH2 3RW. Ground Capacity: 2,500 Seating Capacity: 200. Tel. No: (0191) 388-3363

CONSETT AFC
Founded: 1899 Nickname: 'The Steelmen' Former Name: Consett Celtic FC. Ground: Belle Vue Park, Ashdale Road, Consett, Co. Durham. Ground Capacity: 9,000 Seating Capacity: 474. Tel. No: (01207) 503788

CROOK TOWN FC
Founded: 1889 Nickname: None Ground: Millfield Ground, West Road, Crook, Co. Durham. Ground Capacity: 4,000 Seating Capacity: 400. Tel. No: (01388) 762959; (01388) 762026 (Secretary)

DUNSTON FEDERATION BREWERY FC
Founded: 1975 Nickname: 'The Fed' Ground: Federation Park, Wellington Road, Dunston, Gateshead, Tyne & Wear. Ground Capacity: 2,500 Seating Capacity: 200 Tel.: (0191) 493-2935 (Ground); (0191) 267-2250 (Sec)

DURHAM CITY AFC
Founded: 1918 (Reformed 1950) Nickname: 'The Citizens' Ground: New Ferens Park, Belmont, Durham. Ground Capacity: 3,900 Seating Capacity: 300. Tel. No: (0191) 386-9616

EPPLETON COLLIERY WELFARE FC
Founded: 1929 Nickname: 'The Welfare' Ground: Welfare Park, Eppleton, Hetton-le-Hole, Tyne & Wear. Ground Capacity: 2,000 Seating Capacity: 50. Tel. No: (0191) 526-0080 (Sec.); (0191) 526-1048 (Ground)

FERRYHILL ATHLETIC FC
Founded: 1921 Nickname: 'The Hill' 'The Latics' Ground: Darlington Road, Ferryhill, Co. Durham Ground Capacity: 6,000 Seating Capacity: 400. Tel. No: (01740) 651937

GUISBOROUGH TOWN FC
Founded: 1973 Nickname: 'Priorymen' Ground: King George V Playing Fields, Howlbeck Road, Guisborough, Cleveland. Ground Capacity: 3,500 Seating Capacity: 150 Tel.: (01287) 638993 (Secretary); (01287) 636925 (Ground)

MURTON AFC
Founded: 1891 Nickname: None Former Names: Murton Red Star FC, Murton Colliery Wanderers FC. Ground: Recreation Park, Church Lane, Murton, Co.

Durham. Ground Capacity: 3,500 Seating Capacity: 100. Tel. No: (0191) 5170814

PETERLEE NEWTOWN FC
Founded: 1976 Nickname: 'Newtowners' Ground: Eden Lane, Peterlee, Co. Durham. Ground Capacity: 2,000 Seating Capacity: 50. Tel. No: (0191) 581-4591 (Sec); (0191) 586-3004 (Ground); (0191) 586-4415 (Office)

R.T.M. FC
Founded: 1930 Nickname: 'Star' Former Name: Blue Star Welfare FC, Newcastle Blue Star FC. Ground: Wheatsheaf Sports Ground, Woolsington, Newcastle-upon-Tyne. Ground Capacity: 2,000. Seating Capacity: 250. Tel. No: (0191) 286-0425

SEAHAM RED STAR FC
Founded: 1973 Nickname: None Ground: Seaham Town Park, Seaham, County Durham Ground Capacity: 2,000 Seating Capacity: 80. Tel. No: (0191) 513-0880

SHILDON FC
Founded: 1890 Nickname: 'The Railwaymen' Ground: Dean Street, Shildon, Co. Durham. Ground Capacity: 4,000 Seating Capacity: 350. Tel. No: (01325) 316322 (Secretary); (01388) 773877 (Ground)

STOCKTON FC
Founded: 1980 Nickname: None Ground: Teesdale Park, Acklam Road, Middlesbrough, Cleveland. Ground Capacity: 3,000 Seating Capacity: None Tel. No: (01642) 670779 (Secretary); (01642) 606803 (Ground)

TOW LAW TOWN FC
Founded: 1890 Nickname: 'Lawyers' Ground: Ironworks Road, Tow Law, Bishop Auckland, County Durham. Ground Capacity: 3,000 Seating Capacity: 500. Tel. No: (01388) 731443

WEST AUCKLAND TOWN FC
Founded: 1893 Nickname: 'West' Ground: Darlington Road Ground, West Auckland. Ground Capacity: 2,500 Seating Capacity: 200. Tel. No: (01388) 833783

WHICKHAM FC
Founded: 1943 Nickname: None Ground: Glebe Ground, Rectory Lane, Whickham, Newcastle-upon-Tyne, Tyne & Wear. Ground Capacity: 3,000 Seating Capacity: 60 Tel. No: (0191) 488-3054 (Ground); (0191) 488-644 (Secretary)

WHITBY TOWN FC
Founded: 1893 Nickname: 'The Seasiders' 'The Blues' Ground: Turnbull Ground, Upgang Lane, Whitby. Ground Capacity: 4,500 Seating Capacity: 250. Tel. No: (01947) 604847 (Secretary); (01947) 603193 (Ground)

CARLING NORTH WEST COUNTIES DIV. 1

BLACKPOOL WREN ROVERS FC
Founded: 1936 **Nickname**: 'Wrens' **Ground**: School Road, Marton, Blackpool, Lancs. **Ground Capacity**: 1,500 **Seating Capacity**: 500. **Tel. No**: (01253) 760570

BOOTLE FC
Founded: 1953. **Nickname**: 'The Bucks' **Ground**: Bucks Park, Northern Perimeter Road, Netherton, Bootle, L30 7PT. **Ground Capacity**: 4,000 **Seating Capacity**: 350 **Tel. No**: (0151) 527-1851

BURSCOUGH FC
Founded: 1946 **Nickname**: 'The Linnets' **Ground**: Victoria Park, Mart Lane, Burscough, Ormskirk, Lancs. L40 0SD. **Ground Capacity**: 3,500 **Seating Capacity**: 300. **Tel. No**: (01704) 893237

CHADDERTON FC
Founded: 1947 **Nickname**: 'Chaddy' **Former Names**: Millbrow FC, North Chadderton Amateurs FC. **Ground**: 'Broadway', Andrew Street, Chadderton, Oldham, Lancs. **Ground Capacity**: 2,500 **Seating Capacity**: 200. **Tel. No**: (0161) 678-9624 (Secretary)

CLITHEROE FC
Founded: 1877 **Nickname**: 'The Blues' **Former Name**: Clitheroe Central FC. **Ground**: Shawbridge, Pendle Road, Clitheroe, Lancs. **Ground Capacity**: 4,000 **Seating Capacity**: 200. **Tel. No**: (01200) 24370 (Secretary)

DARWEN FC
Founded: 1875 **Nickname**: 'Anchormen' **Ground**: Anchor Ground, Anchor Road, Darwen, Lancs. **Ground Capacity**: 4,000 **Seating Capacity**: 230. **Tel. No**: (01254) 705627

EASTWOOD HANLEY FC
Founded: 1946 **Nickname**: 'Blues' **Ground**: Hollinwood Road, Kidsgrove, Stoke, Staffs. **Ground Capacity**: 3,000 **Seating Capacity**: 400. **Tel. No**: (01782) 279062 (Secretary); (01782) 274238 (Ground) Eastwood Hanley are groundsharing with Kidsgrove Ath.

FLIXTON FC
Founded: 1960 **Nickname**: None. **Ground**: Valley Road, Flixton, Manchester. **Ground Capacity**: 3,000 **Seating Capacity**: 500. **Tel. No**: (0161) 748-2903; (0161) 865-0418 (Secretary)

GLOSSOP NORTH END AFC
Founded: 1886 **Nickname**: 'The Hillmen' **Former Names**: Glossop AFC, Glossop N.E. **Ground**: Surrey Street, Glossop, SK13 9AJ. **Ground Capacity**: 2,239 **Seating Capacity**: 250. **Tel. No**: (01457) 863852

HOLKER OLD BOYS FC
Founded: 1936 **Nickname**: 'Cobs' **Ground**: Rakesmoor Lane, Howcoat, Barrow-in-Furness, Cumbria. **Ground Capacity**: 2,500 **Seating Capacity**: 40. **Tel. No**: (01229) 828176 (Ground)

KIDSGROVE ATHLETIC FC
Founded: 1952 **Nickname**: 'Athletic' **Ground**: Hollinwood Road, Kidsgrove, Stoke, Staffs. **Ground Capacity**: 3,000 **Seating Capacity**: 400 **Tel. No**: (01782) 782412

MAINE ROAD FC
Founded: 1955 **Nickname**: 'The Blues' **Former Name**: City Supporters (Rusholme) FC. **Ground**: Manchester County F.A. Ground, Brantingham Road, Chorlton, Manchester M21 1TG **Ground Capacity**: 2,000 **Seating Capacity**: 200. **Tel. No**: (0161) 226-9937

MOSSLEY FC
Founded: 1903 **Nickname**: 'The Lilywhites' **Former Names**: Park Villa FC, Mossley Juniors FC. **Ground**: Seel Park, Market Street, Mossley, Ashton-under-Lyne, Lancashire. **Ground Capacity**: 8,000 **Seating Capacity**: 200 **Tel. No**: (01457) 832369

NANTWICH TOWN FC
Founded: 1884 **Nickname**: 'The Dabbers' **Ground**: Jackson Avenue, off London Road, Nantwich, Cheshire. **Ground Capacity**: 1,500. **Seating Capacity**: 187. **Tel. No**: (01270) 624098

NEWCASTLE TOWN FC
Founded: 1964 **Nickname**: 'Castle' **Former Name**: Parkway Hanley FC. **Ground**: Lyme Valley Parkway Stadium, Clayton, Newcastle-under-Lyme, Staffs. **Ground Capacity**: 4,000 **Seating Capacity**: 300. **Tel.**: (01782) 333445 (Secretary); (01782) 662351 (Ground)

PENRITH FC
Founded: 1894. **Nickname**: 'The Blues' **Ground**: Southead Road, Penrith. **Ground Capacity**: 3,000 **Seating Capacity**: 250. **Tel. No**: (01768) 862551 (Secretary)

PRESCOT AFC
Founded: 1884. **Nickname**: 'The Tigers' **Former Names**: Prescot Cables FC, Prescot Town FC. **Ground**: Sandra Park, Hope Street, Prescot, Merseyside. **Ground Capacity**: 2,000 **Seating**: 500. **Tel.No**: (0151) 430-0507

ROSSENDALE UNITED FC
Founded: 1898 **Nickname**: 'The Stags' **Ground**: Dark Lane, Staghills Road, Newchurch, Rossendale. **Ground Capacity**: 2,200 **Seating**: 400 **Tel.**: (01706) 215119

ST. HELENS TOWN AFC
Founded: 1903 (Reformed 1946) **Nickname**: 'The Town' **Ground**: Hoghton Road, Sutton, St. Helens, Merseyside. **Ground Capacity**: 4,400 **Seating Capacity**: 200. **Tel. No**: (01744) 812721

SALFORD CITY FC
Founded: 1940 **Nickname**: 'City' **Ground**: Moor Lane, Kersal, Salford, Manchester. **Ground Capacity**: 8,000 **Seating Capacity**: 600. **Tel. No**: (0161) 792-6287

SKELMERSDALE UNITED FC
Founded: 1882. **Nickname**: 'The Skemmers' **Ground**: White Moss Park, White Moss Road, Skelmersdale, Lancs. **Ground Capacity**: 10,000 **Seating Capacity**: 250. **Tel. No**: (01704) 894504

TRAFFORD FC
Founded: 1990 **Nickname**: 'The North' **Former Name**: North Trafford FC **Ground**: Shawe View, Shawe Road off Chassen Road, Flixton, Urmston, Manchester M41 **Ground Capacity**: 2,500 **Seating Capacity**: 284 **Tel. No**: (0161) 746-9726 (Sec.); (0161) 747-1727 (Ground)

ATHERSTONE UNITED FC

Founded: 1979	**Colours**: Shirts - Red & White Stripes
Former Name(s): None	Shorts - Red
Nickname: 'The Adders'	**Telephone No.**: (01827) 717829
Ground: Sheepy Road, Atherstone,	**Daytime Phone No.**: (01203) 351188
Warwickshire	**Pitch Size**: 115 × 80yds
Office Address: 19 Hathaway Drive, Nuneaton	**Ground Capacity**: 3,500
Warwicks	**Seating Capacity**: 353
Record Attendance: 2,588	

GENERAL INFORMATION
Supporters Club Administrator: J. Harman
Address: 57 Newton Gardens, Great Barr, Birmingham B43 5DX
Telephone Number: -
Car Parking: Adjacent to Ground
Coach Parking: Adjacent to Ground
Nearest Railway Station: Atherstone (1 ml)
Nearest Bus Station: Atherstone/Nuneaton
Club Shop: At Ground
Opening Times: Matchdays Only
Telephone No.: (01827) 717829
Postal Sales: -
Nearest Police Station: Atherstone 200 yards
Police Force: Warwicks
Police Telephone No.: -

GROUND INFORMATION
Away Supporters' Entrances: Gipsy Lane
Away Supporters' Sections: Gipsy Lane
Family Facilities: **Location of Stand**:
None specified
Capacity of Stand: -

ADMISSION INFO (1995/96 PRICES)
Adult Standing: £4.00
Adult Seating: £4.50
Child Standing: £2.00
Child Seating: £2.25
Programme Price: £1.00
FAX Number: None

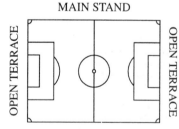

MAIN STAND

OPEN TERRACE

OPEN TERRACE

COVERED TERRACE

Travelling Supporters Information:
Routes: Take A5 into Town. Follow directions for Twycross Sheepy Magna - ground 0.5 mile on left.

BALDOCK TOWN FC

Founded: 1889
Former Name(s): None
Nickname: 'Reds'
Ground: Norton Road, Baldock, Hertfordshire, SG7 5AU
Record Attendance: 1,200 vs Arsenal (1983)
Colours: Shirts - Red
       Shorts - White

Telephone No.: (01462) 895449
Contact Address: Cyril T. Hammond, 2 Elmwood Court, 65 High Street, Baldock, Hertfordshire   SG7 6AY
Contact Phone No.: (01462) 894253
Pitch Size: 113 × 74yds
Ground Capacity: 3,000
Seating Capacity: 300

GENERAL INFORMATION
Supporters Club Administrator: None
Address: -
Telephone Number: -
Car Parking: At Ground
Coach Parking: At Ground
Nearest Railway Station: Baldock (0.5 mile)
Nearest Bus Station: Baldock
Club Shop: Yes
Opening Times: Matchdays Only
Telephone No.: -
Postal Sales: Yes
Nearest Police Station: Baldock
Police Force: Hertfordshire
Police Telephone No.: -

GROUND INFORMATION
Away Supporters' Entrances: No usual segregation
Away Supporters' Sections: No usual segregation

ADMISSION INFO (1995/96 PRICES)
Adult Standing: £4.00
Adult Seating: £4.00
Child Standing: £2.50
Child Seating: £2.50
Programme Price: £1.00
FAX Number: (01462) 490177

(CLUBHOUSE)
MAIN STAND

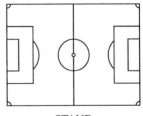

STAND

Travelling Supporters Information:
Routes: From Midlands & North: Exit M1 at junction 13 and take A507 to Stotfold. At Stotfold take right for Letchworth then left along Norton Road to Baldock. Ground is on left before Railway Bridge; From Elsewhere: Exit A1(M) junction 9 and follow A6141 to A505, look for Baldock sign and take 3rd exit at roundabout into Baldock Road. After 3 miles turn left at Orange Tree pub. Ground on right after railway bridge.

BURTON ALBION FC

Founded: 1950
Former Name(s): None
Nickname: 'The Brewers'
Ground: Eton Park, Princess Way, Burton-on-Trent   DE14 2RU
Record Attendance: 5,860 (1964)

Colours: Shirts - Yellow & Black
Shorts - Yellow & Black
Telephone No.: (01283) 565938
Daytime Phone No.: (01283) 565938
Pitch Size: 110 × 72yds
Ground Capacity: 5,000
Seating Capacity: 296

GENERAL INFORMATION
Supporters Club Administrator:
Pete Thomas
Address: 67 Hunter Street, Burton-on-Trent, Staffs   DE14 2SR
Telephone Number: (01283) 511983
Car Parking: At Ground (300 cars)
Coach Parking: At Ground
Nearest Railway Station: Burton-on-Trent (1 mile)
Nearest Bus Station: Burton-on-Trent (1 ml)
Club Shop: Yes
Opening Times: Matchdays Only
Telephone No.: (01283) 565938
Postal Sales: -
Nearest Police Station: Burton (1 mile)
Police Force: Staffordshire
Police Telephone No.: (01283) 565011

GROUND INFORMATION
Away Supporters' Entrances: Derby Road
Away Supporters' Sections: Gordon Bray Terrace
Family Facilities: Location of Stand: None Specified
Capacity of Stand: -

ADMISSION INFO (1995/96 PRICES)
Adult Standing: £3.50
Adult Seating: £4.50
Child Standing: £1.00
Child Seating: £2.00
Programme Price: 80p
FAX Number: (01283) 512425

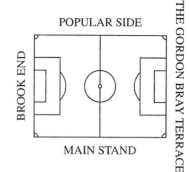

Travelling Supporters Information:
Routes: From the North: Exit the M1 at junction 28 and follow the A38 towards Burton. Take the turning onto A5121 and follow into Burton. Turn right at the island and the ground is on the left; From South: Exit the M1 at junction 22 and follow the A50 towards Burton. Once in Burton go over Trent Bridge and through 3 sets of traffic lights. Turn right at the mini island and continue to the next island where turn left, entrance to the ground is on the left.

CAMBRIDGE CITY FC

Founded: 1908
Former Name(s): Cambridge Town FC
Nickname: 'City Devils'
Ground: City Ground, Milton Road,
Cambridge CB4 1UY
Record Attendance: 12,000 (1950)

Colours: Shirts - White
    Shorts - Black
Telephone No.: (01223) 357973
Daytime Phone No.: (01223) 357973
Pitch Size: 110 × 71yds
Ground Capacity: 5,000
Seating Capacity: 495

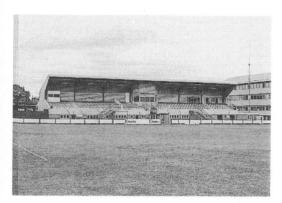

GENERAL INFORMATION
Supporters Club Administrator:
Terry Dunn
Address: City Ground, Cambridge
Telephone Number: (01223) 357973
Car Parking: At Ground (200 cars)
Coach Parking: At Ground
Nearest Railway Station: Cambridge (2 mls)
Nearest Bus Station: Cambridge
Club Shop: Yes
Opening Times: Matchdays Only
Telephone No.: (01223) 357973
Postal Sales: Yes
Nearest Police Station: Park Side,
Cambridge
Police Force: Mid Anglia
Police Telephone No.: (01223) 358966

GROUND INFORMATION
Away Supporters' Entrances: No Segregation
Away Supporters' Sections: No Segregation
Family Facilities: Location of Stand:
None Specified
Capacity of Stand: -

ADMISSION INFO (1995/96 PRICES)
Adult Standing: £4.00
Adult Seating: £4.00
Child Standing: £2.00
Child Seating: £2.00
Programme Price: 60p
FAX Number: None

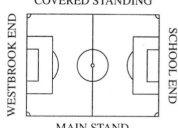

ALLOTMENT SIDE
COVERED STANDING

WESTBROOK END

SCHOOL END

MAIN STAND
CLUBHOUSE

Travelling Supporters Information:
Routes: Exit M11 junction 13 and take A1303 into the city. At the end of Madingley Road, turn left into Chesterton Lane and then Chesterton Road. Go into the one-way system and turn left onto Milton Road (A10) - ground is on the left.

CHELMSFORD CITY FC

Founded: 1938
Former Name(s): Chelmsford FC (1878-1938)
Nickname: 'City'
Ground: The Stadium, New Writtle Street, Chelmsford, Essex   CM2 0RP
Record Attendance: 16,807 (10/9/49)

Colours: Shirts - Claret
Shorts - Claret
Telephone No.: (01245) 353052
Daytime Phone No.: (01245) 353052
Pitch Size: 112 × 74yds
Ground Capacity: 2,850
Seating Capacity: 1,296

GENERAL INFORMATION
Supporters Club Administrator:
D. Southwood
Address: 57 Heath Drive, Chelmsford, Essex   CM2 9HE
Telephone Number: (01245) 260186
Car Parking: Council Car Park adjacent to Cricket Ground End
Coach Parking: Street Parking
Nearest Railway Station: Chelmsford (0.5 mile)
Nearest Bus Station: Chelmsford (0.5 mile)
Club Shop: At Ground
Opening Times: One hour before games, half-time and 15 minutes after a game
Telephone No.: -
Postal Sales: Yes
Nearest Police Station: Chelmsford
Police Force: Essex
Police Telephone No.: (01245) 491212

GROUND INFORMATION
Away Supporters' Entrances: Usually no segregation
Away Supporters' Sections: Otherwise Wolseley End

ADMISSION INFO (1995/96 PRICES)
Adult Standing: £4.00
Adult Seating: £5.00
Child Standing: £2.00
Child Seating: £2.50
Programme Price: £1.00
FAX Number: None

OLD BARN ENCLOSURE

WOLSELEY END

CRICKET GROUND END

NEW WRITTLE STREET

Travelling Supporters Information:
Routes: From A12: Take A1016 (Chelmsford) exit and follow Colchester signs. At the 3rd roundabout, turn left onto B1007, New London Road. At the 2nd set of traffic lights turn left (signed County Cricket Ground). Ground is 100 yards on the right.

CHELTENHAM TOWN FC

Founded: 1892
Former Name(s): None
Nickname: 'Robins'
Ground: Whaddon Road, Cheltenham, Gloucestershire   GL52 5NA
Record Attendance: 8,326 (1956)

Colours: Shirts - Red & White Stripes
Shorts - Navy & White
Telephone No.: (01242) 573558
Daytime Phone No.: (01242) 573558/513397
Pitch Size: 110 × 73yds
Ground Capacity: 6,000
Seating Capacity: 1,200

GENERAL INFORMATION
Supporters Club Administrator:
John Regan, Robins Benefit Committee
Address: c/o Club
Telephone Number: (01242) 573558
Car Parking: At Ground (120 spaces)
Coach Parking: Wymans Road
Nearest Railway Station: Cheltenham Spa (2 miles)
Nearest Bus Station: Cheltenham Royal Well
Club Shop:
Opening Times: Matchdays Only & Office during week
Telephone No.: (01242) 521974
Postal Sales: Yes
Nearest Police Station: Whaddon, Cheltenham
Police Force: Gloucestershire
Police Telephone No.: (01242) 528282

GROUND INFORMATION
Away Supporters' Entrances: Wymans Road Side
Away Supporters' Sections: (Only certain matches)
Family Facilities: Location of Stand:
Gulf Oil Enclosure
Capacity of Stand: 1,200

ADMISSION INFO (1995/96 PRICES)
Adult Standing: £4.00
Adult Seating: £5.00 and £6.00
Child Standing: £2.50
Child Seating: £3.00 and £4.00
Programme Price: £1.00
FAX Number: (01242) 224675

WYMANS ROAD SIDE

PRESTBURY ROAD

WHADDON ROAD END

MAIN STAND & CAR PARK

Travelling Supporters Information:
Routes: The Ground is situated to the North-East of Cheltenham, 1 mile from the Town Centre off the B4632 (Prestbury Road) - Whaddon Road is to the East of the B4632 just North of Pittville Circus.

CRAWLEY TOWN FC

Founded: 1896
Former Name(s): None
Nickname: 'The Reds'
Ground: Town Mead, Ifield Avenue, West Green, Crawley, West Sussex   RH11 7HP
Record Attendance: 4,200 (1991)

Colours: Shirts - Red
Shorts - Red
Telephone No.: (01293) 410000
Daytime Phone No.: (01293) 410001
Pitch Size: 110 × 73yds
Ground Capacity: 4,750
Seating Capacity: 400

GENERAL INFORMATION
Supporters Club Administrator:
Allan Harper
Address: 33 Nuthurst Close, Ifield, Crawley, Sussex
Telephone Number: (01293) 511764
Car Parking: Car Park at Ground (100 cars)
Coach Parking: Car Park at Ground
Nearest Railway Station: Crawley (0.75 ml)
Nearest Bus Station: By Railway Station
Club Shop: At Ground
Opening Times: Matchdays Only 1.30pm - 5.30pm & 6.30 - 9.30pm
Telephone No.: (01293) 410009
Postal Sales: Yes
Nearest Police Station: Kilnmead, Northgate (800 yards)
Police Force: Sussex
Police Telephone No.: (01293) 524242

GROUND INFORMATION
Away Supporters' Entrances: Fire Station End
Away Supporters' Sections: Fire Station End
Family Facilities: Location of Stand:
None specified
Capacity of Stand: -
ADMISSION INFO (1995/96 PRICES)
Adult Standing: £4.00
Adult Seating: £5.00
Child Standing: £2.00
Child Seating: £3.00
Programme Price: £1.00
FAX Number: (01293) 410002

Travelling Supporters Information:
Routes: Exit M23 at junction 10 and take A2011 towards Crawley. Take 3rd exit at roundabout, keeping to the Ring Road. Turn left at the next roundabout into London Road, then second right into Ifield Avenue, ground is next to the fire station.

DORCHESTER TOWN FC

Founded: 1880	**Colours**: Shirts - Black & White Stripes
Former Name(s): None	Shorts - Black
Nickname: 'The Magpies'	**Telephone No.**: (01305) 262451/267623
Ground: The Avenue Stadium, Weymouth	**Daytime Phone No.**: (01305) 262451/262527
Avenue, Dorchester, Dorset DT1 2RY	**Pitch Size**: 110 × 80yds
Record Attendance: 4,040 (15/10/90)	**Ground Capacity**: 7,210
	Seating Capacity: 710

GENERAL INFORMATION
Supporters Club Administrator:
H.G. Gill
Address: 39 Thatcham Pk., Yeovil, Somerset
Telephone Number: (01935) 26029
Car Parking: Car Park at Ground (350 cars)
Coach Parking: At Ground
Nearest Railway Station: Dorchester South & West (both 1 mile)
Nearest Bus Station: Nearby
Club Shop: Yes
Opening Times: During all 1st Team Games
Telephone No.: (01305) 262451
Postal Sales: Yes
Nearest Police Station: Weymouth Avenue, Dorchester
Police Force: Dorset
Police Telephone No.: (01305) 251212

GROUND INFORMATION
Away Supporters' Entrances: Main Stand Side
Away Supporters' Sections: Not Usually Segregated
Family Facilities: Location of Stand:
None specified
Capacity of Stand: -

ADMISSION INFO (1995/96 PRICES)
Adult Standing: £4.00
Adult Seating: £4.50
Child Standing: £2.20
Child Seating: £2.70
Programme Price: £1.00
FAX Number: (01305) 251569

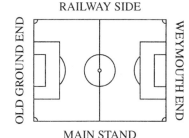

Travelling Supporters Information:
Routes: Take Dorchester Bypass (A35) from all directions, ground is on South side of Town adjacent to roundabout at intersection with A354 to Weymouth. Alternatively take Weymouth signs from Town Centre (1.5 miles).

GLOUCESTER CITY FC

Founded: 1883
Former Name(s): Gloucester YMCA
Nickname: 'The Tigers'
Ground: Meadow Park, Sudmeadow Road,
Hempstead, Gloucester   GL2 6HS
Record Attendance: 5,000 (1990)

Colours: Shirts - Yellow
Shorts - Black
Telephone No.: (01452) 523883
Daytime Phone No.: (01452) 523883
Pitch Size: 112 × 72yds
Ground Capacity: 5,000
Seating Capacity: 560

GENERAL INFORMATION
Supporters Club Administrator: D.Carlisle
Address: c/o Club
Telephone Number: (01452) 523883
Car Parking: Car Park at Ground (150 cars)
Coach Parking: At Ground
Nearest Railway Station: Gloucester (2 mls)
Nearest Bus Station: Gloucester
Club Shop: Yes
Opening Times: Matchdays Only
Telephone No.: (01452) 381761
Postal Sales: Yes
Nearest Police Station: Gloucester
Police Force: Gloucestershire Constabulary
Police Telephone No.: (01452) 521201

GROUND INFORMATION
Away Supporters' Entrances: Segregation is an
option but is normally not used
Away Supporters' Sections: -
Family Facilities: Location of Stand:
None specified
Capacity of Stand: -

ADMISSION INFO (1995/96 PRICES)
Adult Standing: £4.00
Adult Seating: £5.00
Child Standing: £2.00
Child Seating: £3.00
Programme Price: £1.00
FAX Number: (01452) 301330

```
                    MAIN STAND
   ┌─────────────────────────────────────┐
 O │    ┌───┐         ┌─┐         ┌───┐    │ O
 P │    │   │        (   )        │   │    │ P
 E │    │   │         └─┘         │   │    │ E
 N │    └───┘                     └───┘    │ N
   │                                       │
 T │                                       │ T
 E │                                       │ E
 R │                                       │ R
 R │                                       │ R
 A │                                       │ A
 C │                                       │ C
 E └─────────────────────────────────────┘ E
              COVERED TERRACE
```

Travelling Supporters Information:
Routes: Take A40 into the City Centre towards historic docks, then Severn Road, right into Hempstead Lane
then second right into Sudmeadow Road. Ground 50 yards on left.

GRAVESEND & NORTHFLEET FC

Founded: 1946
Former Name(s): Formed by Amalgamation of
Gravesend United FC & Northfleet United FC
Nickname: 'The Fleet'
Ground: Stonebridge Road, Northfleet,
Gravesend, Kent   DA11 9BA
Record Attendance: 12,063 (1963)

Colours: Shirts - Red
   Shorts - White
Telephone No.: (01474) 533796
Contact No.: (01474) 363424
Pitch Size: 112 × 72yds
Ground Capacity: 3,300
Seating Capacity: 600

GENERAL INFORMATION
Supporters Club Administrator:
Mick Baines
Address: c/o Club
Telephone Number: (01474) 352501
Car Parking: Car Park at Ground (450 cars)
Coach Parking: At Ground
Nearest Railway Station: Northfleet (5 mins)
Nearest Bus Station: Bus Stop outside
ground (From Gravesend & Dartford)
Club Shop: At Ground
Opening Times: Matchdays Only
Telephone No.: (01474) 533796
Postal Sales: Yes, c/o Club
Nearest Police Station: Gravesend (3 miles)
Police Force: Gravesend
Police Telephone No.: (01474) 564346

GROUND INFORMATION
Away Supporters' Entrances: No Segregation
Away Supporters' Sections: No Segregation
Family Facilities: Location of Stand:
None specified
Capacity of Stand: -

ADMISSION INFO (1995/96 PRICES)
Adult Standing: £4.00
Adult Seating: £5.00 or £6.00
Child Standing: £2.00
Child Seating: £2.50 or £3.00
Programme Price: £1.00
FAX Number: (01474) 363424

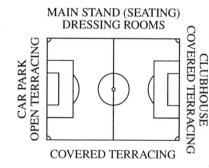

Travelling Supporters Information:
Routes: Take A2 to Northfleet/Southfleet exit along B262 to Northfleet then B2175 (Springhead Road) to
the Junction with the A226. Turn left (The Hill, Northfleet) and follow road (Stonebridge Road). Ground is
1 mile on the right at foot of steep hill.

GRESLEY ROVERS FC

Founded: 1882
Former Name(s): None
Nickname: 'The Moatmen'
Ground: The Moat Ground, Moat Street,
Church Gresley, Swadlincote, Derbyshire
Record Attendance: 3,950 (1957-58)
Correspondence Address: c/o Neil Betteridge,
88 Midway Road, Swadlincote, Derbyshire

Colours: Shirts - Red with White Sleeves
Shorts - Red
Telephone No.: (01283) 216315
Daytime Phone No.: (01283) 221881
Pitch Size: 110 × 70yds
Ground Capacity: 2,500
Seating Capacity: 415

GENERAL INFORMATION
Supporters Club Administrator: -
Address: c/o Club
Telephone Number: (01283) 216315
Car Parking: At Ground
Coach Parking: At Ground
Nearest Railway Station: Burton-on-Trent (5 miles)
Nearest Bus Station: Swadlincote (1 mile)
Club Shop: Yes
Opening Times: Matchdays Only
Telephone No.: (01283) 216315
Postal Sales: Yes
Nearest Police Station: Swadlincote
Police Force: Derbyshire
Police Telephone No.: (01283) 550101

GROUND INFORMATION
Away Supporters' Entrances: Moat Street or Church Street
Away Supporters' Sections: Not applicable
Family Facilities: Location of Stand:
None specified
Capacity of Stand: -

ADMISSION INFO (1995/96 PRICES)
Adult Standing: £4.00
Adult Seating: £4.00
Child Standing: £2.00
Child Seating: £2.00
Programme Price: 70p
FAX Number: (01283) 221881

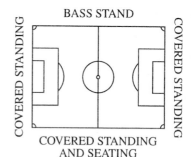

Travelling Supporters Information:
Routes: Take the M42 to A444 Burton-on-Trent exit and head for Castle Gresley. In Castle Gresley at large island, turn right onto the A514 (signposted Church Gresley). Turn right at the top of the hill (Miners Arms) then first left into Church Street. Take 2nd exit on the left (School Street) and Moat Street is next left.

HALESOWEN TOWN FC

Founded: 1873	**Colours**: Shirts - Blue
Former Name(s): None	Shorts - Blue
Nickname: 'The Yeltz'	**Telephone No.**: (0121) 550-2179
Ground: The Grove, Old Hawne Lane,	**Daytime Phone No.**: (0121) 550-2179
Halesowen, West Midlands	**Pitch Size**: 110 × 71yds
Record Attendance: 5,000 (19/11/55)	**Ground Capacity**: 5,000
	Seating Capacity: 420

GENERAL INFORMATION
Supporters Club Administrator: Paul Floud
Address: 112 Blackberry Lane, Halesowen
Telephone Number: (0121) 550-8999
Car Parking: Room for 70 Cars at Social Club
Coach Parking: Available near Ground
Nearest Railway Station: Old Hill (2 miles)
Nearest Bus Station: On main Stourbridge Road.
Club Shop: Yes
Opening Times: Matchdays Only
Telephone No.: (0121) 550-2179
Postal Sales: Yes
Nearest Police Station: Halesowen
Police Force: West Midlands
Police Telephone No.: (0121) 626-8030

GROUND INFORMATION
Away Supporters' Entrances: No Segregation
Away Supporters' Sections: No Segregation
Family Facilities: Location of Stand:
Harry Rudge Stand
Capacity of Stand: 380

ADMISSION INFO (1995/96 PRICES)
Adult Standing: £4.00
Adult Seating: £4.80
Child Standing: £1.00
Child Seating: £1.80
Programme Price: £1.00
FAX Number: None
OAP Standing: £2.00
OAP Seating: £2.80

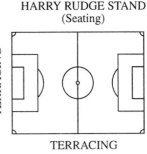

Travelling Supporters Information:
Routes: Exit M5 at junction 3, follow A456 towards Kidderminster to 1st Island and turn right at the signpost onto the A458 towards Dudley. Turn left at the next island and follow the signpost onto A458 towards Stourbridge. At the next island take the 3rd exit, the ground is approximately 400 yards on the left.

HASTINGS TOWN FC

Founded: 1894
Former Name(s): Hastings & St. Leonards Amateurs
Nickname: 'The Town'
Ground: The Pilot Field, Elphinstone Road, Hastings TN34 2AX
Record Attendance: 2,248 (1992/93)

Colours: Shirts - White with Red Trim
     Shorts - White with Red Trim
Telephone No.: (01424) 444635/430517
Daytime Phone No.: (01424) 444635
Pitch Size: 110 × 78yds
Ground Capacity: 10,000
Seating Capacity: 900

GENERAL INFORMATION
Supporters Club Administrator:
R. A. Cosens
Address: 22 Baldslow Road, Hastings TN34 2EZ
Telephone Number: (01424) 427867
Car Parking: Car Park
Coach Parking: On Street
Nearest Railway Station: Hastings (1.5 mls)
Nearest Bus Station: Town Centre (1.5 miles)
Club Shop: Yes
Opening Times: Match Days Only
Telephone No.: (01424) 430517
Postal Sales: via R. Baker, 35 Edlescombe Road South, St. Leonards-on-Sea
Nearest Police Station: Hastings
Police Force: East Sussex
Police Telephone No.: (01424) 425000

GROUND INFORMATION
Away Supporters' Entrances: No Segregation
Away Supporters' Sections: No Segregation
Family Facilities: Location of Stand: None specified
Capacity of Stand: -

ADMISSION INFO (1995/96 PRICES)
Adult Standing: £4.00
Adult Seating: £5.00
Child Standing: £2.00
Child Seating: £2.50
Programme Price: £1.00
FAX Number: None

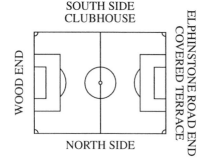

Travelling Supporters Information:
Routes: From A21 turn left into St. Helens Road (A2101). After 1 mile turn left into St. Helens Park Road which leads into Downs Road. Follow Downs Road to the end then turn left at the T-junction. Ground is on the right.

ILKESTON TOWN FC

Founded: 1945	**Colours**: Shirts - Red
Former Name(s): None	Shorts - White
Nickname: 'Robins'	**Telephone No.**: (0115) 932-4094
Ground: New Manor Ground, Awsworth Road	**Pitch Size**: 110 × 72yds
Ilkeston, Derbyshire	**Ground Capacity**: 3,000
Record Attendance: Not Known	**Seating Capacity**: 310

GENERAL INFORMATION
Supporters Club Administrator: None
Address: -
Telephone Number: -
Car Parking: At Ground
Coach Parking: At Ground
Nearest Railway Station: Nottingham (9 miles)
Nearest Bus Station: Heanor
Club Shop: Yes
Opening Times: Matchdays Only
Telephone No.: c/o Club
Postal Sales: Yes
Nearest Police Station: -
Police Force: -
Police Telephone No.: -

GROUND INFORMATION
Away Supporters' Entrances: No Segregation
Away Supporters' Sections: No Segregation
ADMISSION INFO (1995/96 PRICES)
Adult Standing: £4.00
Adult Seating: £4.00
Child Standing: £2.00
Child Seating: £2.00
Programme Price: £1.00
FAX Number: None

CLUBHOUSE

CAR PARK

MAIN STAND
(AWSWORTH ROAD)

Travelling Supporters Information:
Routes: Exit M1 at junction 26 and take the A610 westwards for 2-3 miles. At roundabout turn left to Awsworth then turn right at the The Gardeners pub into Newtons Lane and continue along this into Awsworth Road. Ground is about 1 mile on the left just by the Erewash Canal.

A bypass is to be opened at Awsworth in 1996 and when this is completed it will be necessary to turn before The Gardeners pub into Gin Close to get onto the bypass. This will need to be followed to the first roundabout to get back onto Awsworth Road.

MERTHYR TYDFIL FC

Founded: 1945
Former Name(s): Merthyr Town FC
Nickname: 'Martyrs'
Ground: Penydarren Park, Merthyr Tydfil, Mid Glamorgan
Record Attendance: 21,000 vs Reading, F.A. Cup First Round 1949

Colours: Shirts - White
Shorts - Black
Telephone No.: (01685) 371395
Daytime Phone No.: (01685) 359921
Pitch Size: 110 × 72yds
Ground Capacity: 10,000
Seating Capacity: 1,500

GENERAL INFORMATION
Supporters Club Administrator: Fred Arscott
Address: c/o Club
Telephone Number: (01685) 371395
Car Parking: Street Parking
Coach Parking: Georgetown
Nearest Railway Station: Merthyr Tydfil (0.5 mile)
Nearest Bus Station: Merthyr Tydfil
Club Shop:
Opening Times: Matchdays Only
Telephone No.: (01685) 384102
Postal Sales: Yes
Nearest Police Station: Merthyr Tydfil (0.75 mile)
Police Force: South Wales Constabulary
Police Telephone No.: (01685) 722541

GROUND INFORMATION
Away Supporters' Entrances: Theatre End
Away Supporters' Sections: Theatre End

DISABLED SUPPORTERS INFORMATION
Wheelchairs: Accommodated by Prior Arrangement
Disabled Toilets: None
The Blind: No Special Facilities

ADMISSION INFO (1995/96 PRICES)
Adult Standing: £5.00
Adult Seating: £6.00
Child Standing: £1.00 *
Child Seating: £1.75
Programme Price: £1.00
FAX Number: (01685) 382882
Children under 12 admitted free if with an adult.
* Includes 50p voucher redeemable at Club Shop or Refreshments Cafe

COVERED TERRACING (AWAY)

FAMILY STAND

MAIN STAND

(PANT-MORLAIS ROAD)
THEATRE END

Travelling Supporters Information:
Routes: From East: Take A470 into Merthyr. At top of Merthyr High Street, take sharp left at the lights and then 1st right into Brecon Road. Take the 1st right and then 1st right once again and follow the road into the ground; From North: Leave A465 Heads of the Valleys road for Dowlais. After approximately 2 miles, fork right into Brecon Road, take 1st right and then 1st right once again and follow the road into the ground.

NEWPORT AFC

Founded: 1989	**Colours**: Shirts - Amber with Black Sleeves
Former Name(s): None	Shorts - Amber
Nickname: 'The Exiles'	**Contact No.**: (01633) 271771
Ground: Newport Stadium, Spytty Park,	**Pitch Size**: 112 × 72yds
Langland Way, Newport, Gwent NP9 0PT	**Ground Capacity**: 3,340
Record Attendance: 2,400 vs Moreton (was	**Seating Capacity**: 1,240
24,268 for Newport Co. vs Cardiff City 1937)	

GENERAL INFORMATION
Supporters Club Administrator:
Peter Edwards
Address: The King, 76 Somerton Road,
Lliswerry, Newport, Gwent
Telephone Number: (01633) 271771
Car Parking: At Ground (500 cars)
Coach Parking: At Ground
Nearest Railway Station: Newport
Nearest Bus Station: Newport
Club Shop: Yes, at The King. Also at ground
on matchdays
Opening Times: Monday, Tuesday, Friday
10.00am - 3.15pm
Telephone No.: (01633) 271771
Postal Sales: Enquiries to The King
Nearest Police Station: Maindee
Police Force: Gwent Constabulary
Police Telephone No.: (01633) 244999

DISABLED SUPPORTERS INFORMATION
Wheelchairs: Accommodated by arrangement
Disabled Toilets: None
The Blind: No Special Facilities

ADMISSION INFO (1995/96 PRICES)
Adult Standing: £3.50
Adult Seating: £4.50
Child Standing: £2.50
Child Seating: £3.50
Concessionary Standing: £2.50
Concessionary Seating: £3.50
Programme Price: -
FAX Number: -

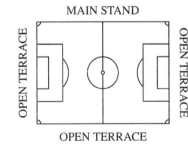

MAIN STAND

OPEN TERRACE

OPEN TERRACE

OPEN TERRACE

Travelling Supporters Information:
Routes: From M4, Junction 24 take the first left off the roundabout, signposted 'Industrial Area'. After about a mile turn left at the roundabout and then straight on at two further roundabouts, turn left and left again into the stadium.

RUSHDEN DIAMONDS FC

Founded: 1992
Former Name(s): Rushden Town FC &
Irthlingborough Diamonds FC
Nickname: 'Diamonds'
Ground: Nene Park, Irthlingborough,
Northants
Record Attendance: 4,375 vs Woking 1995

Colours: Shirts - White with Red & Blue Trim
    Shorts - Blue
Telephone No.: (01933) 650345
Daytime Phone No.: (01933) 650345
Pitch Size: 111 × 74yds
Ground Capacity: 4,500
Seating Capacity: 2,000

GENERAL INFORMATION
Supporters Club Administrator:
Phil Wilton
Address: c/o Club
Telephone Number: (0933) 680035
Car Parking: At Ground
Coach Parking: At Ground
Nearest Railway Station: Wellingborough (5 miles)
Nearest Bus Station: Wellingborough
Club Shop: Yes
Opening Times: Weekdays and Matchdays 9.00-1.00 & 2.00-5.00 (Thursdays 2-5 only)
Telephone No.: (01933) 650345
Postal Sales: Yes
Nearest Police Station: Wellingborough
Police Force: Northamptonshire
Police Telephone No.: (01933) 440333

GROUND INFORMATION
Away Supporters' Entrances: No Segregation
Away Supporters' Sections: -
Family Facilities: **Location of Stand**:
None specified
Capacity of Stand: -
ADMISSION INFO (1995/96 PRICES)
Adult Standing: £4.00
Adult Seating: £4.00
Child Standing: £3.00
Child Seating: £3.00
Programme Price: £1.00
FAX Number: (01933) 650414

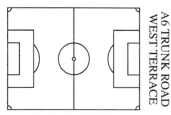

DIAMOND CENTRE
SOUTH STAND

A6 TRUNK ROAD
WEST TERRACE

NORTH STAND

Travelling Supporters Information:
Routes: The ground is located on the A6 about 350 yards north of the junction with the A45 (over bridge).

SALISBURY CITY FC

Founded: 1947	**Colours**: Shirts - White
Former Name(s): Salisbury Corinthian FC &	Shorts - Black
Salisbury FC	**Telephone No.**: (01722) 336689
Nickname: 'The Whites'	**Contact Phone No.**: (01722) 326454
Ground: Victoria Park, Castle Road,	**Pitch Size**: 110 × 72yds
Salisbury, Wiltshire	**Ground Capacity**: 4,000
Record Attendance: 8,903 vs Weymouth	**Seating Capacity**: 320

GENERAL INFORMATION
Supporters Club Administrator: None
Address: -
Telephone Number: -
Car Parking: At Ground
Coach Parking: At Ground
Nearest Railway Station: Salisbury (1.5 mls)
Nearest Bus Station: Salisbury
Club Shop: Yes
Opening Times: Matchdays Only
Telephone No.: -
Postal Sales: Yes
Nearest Police Station: Wilton Road, Salisbury
Police Force: Wiltshire
Police Telephone No.: -

GROUND INFORMATION
Away Supporters' Entrances: No Segregation
Away Supporters' Sections: -

ADMISSION INFO (1995/96 PRICES)
Adult Standing: £4.00
Adult Seating: £4.50
Child Standing: £2.50
Child Seating: £3.00
Programme Price: £1.00
FAX Number: (01722) 326454

MAIN STAND

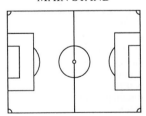

Travelling Supporters Information:
Routes: The ground is situated on the main Salisbury to Amesbury Road (A345) on the northern edge of the city, 1.5 miles from the City Centre.

STAFFORD RANGERS FC

Founded: 1876	**Colours**: Shirts - Black & White Stripes
Former Name(s): None	Shorts - Black
Nickname: 'The Boro'	**Telephone No.**: (01785) 42750
Ground: Marston Road, Stafford ST16 3BX	**Daytime Phone No.**: (01785) 42750
Record Attendance: 8,523 (4/1/75)	**Pitch Size**: 112 × 75yds
	Ground Capacity: 3,472
	Seating Capacity: 426

GENERAL INFORMATION
Supporters Club Administrator:
Chris Elsley
Address: 326 Sandon Road, Stafford
Telephone Number: (01785) 41954
Car Parking: At Ground
Coach Parking: Chell Road, Stafford
Nearest Railway Station: Stafford (2 miles)
Nearest Bus Station: Stafford
Club Shop: Yes
Opening Times: Matchdays Only
Telephone No.: (01785) 42750
Postal Sales: Yes
Nearest Police Station: Stafford
Police Force: Staffs
Police Telephone No.: (01785) 58151

GROUND INFORMATION
Away Supporters' Entrances: Lotus End
Away Supporters' Sections: Lotus End
Family Facilities: Location of Stand:
Junior Rangers Club, Marston Road End
Capacity of Stand: -

ADMISSION INFO (1995/96 PRICES)
Adult Standing: £4.00
Adult Seating: £5.00
Child Standing: £2.00
Child Seating: £3.00
Programme Price: £1.20
FAX Number: (01785) 54050

LOTUS END

ASTONFIELDS ROAD END

TOWN END

MARSTON ROAD END

Travelling Supporters Information:
Routes: Exit M6 junction 14 and take slip road signposted 'Stone/Stafford'. Continue to traffic island and go straight across then take 3rd right into Common Road, signposted 'Common Road/Aston Fields Industrial Estate'. Follow road to bridge and bear left over bridge, ground on right.

SUDBURY TOWN FC

Founded: 1885	**Colours**: Shirts - Yellow
Former Name(s): None	Shorts - Yellow
Nickname: 'The Borough'	**Telephone No.**: (01787) 370957
Ground: Priory Stadium, Priory Walk, Sudbury	**Contact No.**: (01787) 372352
Suffolk CO10 6AP	**Pitch Size**: 110 × 80yds
Record Attendance: 4,700 vs Ipswich Town	**Ground Capacity**: 5,000
(Testimonial) (1978)	**Seating Capacity**: 263

GENERAL INFORMATION
Supporters Club Administrator:
T. Arthur Dalgleish
Address: c/o Club
Telephone Number: (01787) 370957
Car Parking: At Ground
Coach Parking: At Ground
Nearest Railway Station: Sudbury (0.75 ml)
Nearest Bus Station: Sudbury (0.5 mile)
Club Shop: Yes
Opening Times: Matchdays Only
Telephone No.: (01787) 370957
Postal Sales: Yes - via Darren Witt, 4 Highfield Road, Sudbury, Suffolk CO10 6QJ
Nearest Police Station: Sudbury (1 mile)
Police Force: Suffolk
Police Telephone No.: (01284) 774300

GROUND INFORMATION
Away Supporters' Entrances: No Segregation
Away Supporters' Sections: No Segregation

ADMISSION INFO (1995/96 PRICES)
Adult Standing: £4.00
Adult Seating: £4.00
Child Standing: £2.00
Child Seating: £2.00
Programme Price: £1.00
FAX Number: (01787) 379095

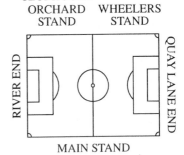

CLUBHOUSE
ORCHARD   WHEELERS
STAND   STAND

RIVER END

QUAY LANE END

MAIN STAND

Travelling Supporters Information:
Routes: From North: Take A134 into town centre then turn into Friar Street. Pass cricket ground and continue to the 'Ship & Star'. Turn left into Priory Walk for ground.

V.S. RUGBY FC

Founded: 1956	**Colours**: Shirts - Dark & Light Blue Stripes
Former Name(s): Valley Sports FC & Valley Sports Rugby FC	Shorts - Navy Blue
	Telephone No.: (01788) 543692
Nickname: 'The Valley'	**Contact No.**: (01788) 540202
Ground: Butlin Road, Rugby, Warwickshire, CV21 3ST	**Pitch Size**: 110 × 80yds
	Ground Capacity: 6,000
Record Attendance: 3,961 (1984)	**Seating Capacity**: 216

GENERAL INFORMATION
Supporters Club Administrator:
Colin Thompson
Address: 62 Wentworth Road, Rugby
Telephone Number: (01788) 561429
Car Parking: 350 Cars at Ground
Coach Parking: At Ground
Nearest Railway Station: Rugby (1 mile)
Nearest Bus Station: Rugby
Club Shop: Yes
Opening Times: Matchdays Only
Telephone No.: (01788) 543692
Postal Sales: Yes
Nearest Police Station: Newbold Road
Police Force: Warwickshire
Police Telephone No.: (01788) 541111

GROUND INFORMATION
Away Supporters' Entrances: No Segregation
Away Supporters' Sections: No Segregation
ADMISSION INFO (1995/96 PRICES)
Adult Standing: £4.00
Adult Seating: £4.50
Child Standing: £2.00
Child Seating: £2.50
Programme Price: £1.00
FAX Number: (01788) 541054

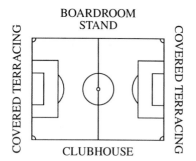

Travelling Supporters Information:
Routes: Exit M6 at junction 1 onto A426 into Rugby. Cross the railway and turn left from Newbold Road into Wood Street. Second right into Railway Terrace then left at end along the B5414, Clifton Road. Butlin Road is about 0.5 mile along, near the Golf Course.

WORCESTER CITY FC

Founded: 1902	**Colours**: Shirts - Blue & White Quarters
Former Name(s): Berwick Rangers	Shorts - Blue
Nickname: 'The City'	**Telephone No.**: (01905) 23003
Ground: St.Georges Lane, Worcester	**Daytime Phone No.**: (01905) 23003
WR1 1QT	**Pitch Size**: 110 × 73yds
Record Attendance: 17,042 (1958/59)	**Ground Capacity**: 10,000
	Seating Capacity: 1,500

GENERAL INFORMATION
Supporters Club Administrator:
John Hawkins
Address: 44 Bromsgrove Street, Barbourne,
Worcester
Telephone Number: -
Car Parking: Street Parking
Coach Parking: Street Parking
Nearest Railway Station: Foregate Street/
Shrub Hill
Nearest Bus Station: Crowngate Bus Station
Club Shop: At Ground
Opening Times: Matchdays (45 mins before
kick-off and during game)
Telephone No.: (01905) 20660
Postal Sales: Contact : John Hawkins,
44 Bromsgrove Street, Barbourne, Worcester
Nearest Police Station: Deansway
Police Force: West Mercia Constabulary
Police Telephone No.: (01905) 723888

GROUND INFORMATION
Away Supporters' Entrances: When segregation -
turnstile at Canal End
Away Supporters' Sections: Canal End
Family Facilities: Location of Stand:
None specified
Capacity of Stand: -

ADMISSION INFO (1995/96 PRICES)
Adult Standing: £4.00
Adult Seating: £4.50
Child Standing: £2.00
Child Seating: £2.50
Programme Price: £1.00
FAX Number: (01905) 26668

BROOKSIDE

BROOKSIDE

CANAL END

MAIN STAND

Travelling Supporters Information:
Routes: From North & East: Exit M5 junction 5 and follow A38 through Droitwich into Worcester. Take a left turn 500 yards after 1st set of traffic lights (signposted); From South & West: Exit M5 junction 7 and follow A44 into Worcester, go past Racecourse and follow A38 towards Bromsgrove. Right turn signposted.

BEAZER HOMES MIDLAND DIVISION

BEDWORTH UNITED FC
Founded: 1896 Nickname: 'The Greenbacks' Former Name: Bedworth Town FC Ground: The Oval, Coventry Road, Bedworth Warwickshire. Ground Capacity: 10,000 Seating Capacity: 300. Tel. No: (01203) 314302

BILSTON TOWN FC
Founded: 1895 Nickname: 'Borough' 'Steelmen' Former Names: Bilston United FC, Bilston FC. Ground: Queen Street, Bilston, West Midlands. Ground Capacity: 5,000 Seating Capacity: 450. Tel. No: (01902) 491498; (01902) 491799 (Secretary)

BRIDGNORTH TOWN FC
Founded: 1946 Nickname: 'The Town' Former Name: St. Leonards Old Boys FC. Ground: Crown Meadow, Innage Lane, Bridgnorth, Shropshire. Ground Capacity: 2,000 Seating Capacity: 250. Tel. No: (01746) 762747

BUCKINGHAM TOWN FC
Founded: 1883 Nickname: 'The Robins' Ground: Ford Meadow, Ford Street, Buckingham, Bucks. Ground Capacity: 4,000 Seating Capacity: 300. Tel. No: (01280) 816257 (Ground); (01280) 815551 (Chairman)

BURY TOWN FC
Founded: 1872 Nickname: 'Blues' Former Name: Bury United FC. Ground: Ram Meadow, Cotton Lane, Bury St. Edmunds, Suffolk. Ground Capacity: 3,500 Seating.: 300 Tel.: (01473) 745640; (01284) 754721

CORBY TOWN FC
Founded: 1948 Nickname: 'The Steelmen' Former Name: Stewarts & Lloyds FC. Ground: Rockingham Triangle Stadium, Rockingham Road, Northants, NN17 2AE. Ground Capacity: 3,000 Seating.: 1,150 Tel.: (01536) 406640; (01536) 522159 (Daytime)

DUDLEY TOWN FC
Founded: 1883 Nickname: 'The Robins' Ground: Round Oak Stadium, John Street, Brierley Hill, West Midlands. Ground Capacity: 2,500 Seating Capacity: 230. Tel. No: (01384) 263478; (01922) 475541 (Sec.)

EVESHAM UNITED FC
Founded: 1945 Nickname: 'The Robins' Former Name: Evesham Town FC. Ground: Common Road, Evesham, Worcs. WR11 4PU. Ground Capacity: 2,000 Seating Capacity: 350. Tel. No: (01386) 442303

GRANTHAM TOWN FC
Founded: 1874 Nickname: 'Gingerbreads' Ground: South Kesteven Stadium, Trent Rd., Grantham, Lincs. Ground Capacity: 7,000 Seats: 750 Tel: (01476) 62011 (01476) 64408 (Sec.); (01476) 593506 (Social Club)

HINCKLEY TOWN FC
Founded: 1958 Nickname: 'Eagles' Former Name: Westfield Rovers FC. Ground: Leicester Road, Hinckley, Leicester. Ground Capacity: 3,000 Seating Capacity: 250. Tel. No: (01455) 615062

KINGS LYNN FC
Founded: 1879 Nickname: 'The Linnetts' Ground: The Walks Stadium, Tennyson Road, Kings Lynn. Ground Capacity: 7,500 Seating Capacity: 1,200. Tel. No: (01733) 267272 (Secretary's Home)

LEICESTER UNITED FC
Founded: 1900 Nickname: 'United' Former Name: Enderby Town FC. Ground: United Park, Winchester Road, Blaby, Leicester LE8 3HN. Ground Capacity: 4,000 Seating Capacity: 228. Tel. No: (01533) 882358

MOOR GREEN FC
Founded: 1901 Nickname: 'The Moors' Ground: The Moorlands, Sherwood Road, Hall Green, Birmingham. Ground Capacity: 3,250 Seating Capacity: 250. Tel. No: (0121) 624-2727 (Ground); (0121) 743-0991 (Day)

NUNEATON BOROUGH FC
Founded: 1937 (Re-formed 1991) Nickname: 'The Borough' Former Name: Nuneaton Town FC. Ground: Manor Park, Beaumont Road, Nuneaton, Warks, CV11 5HD. Ground Capacity: 6,000 Seating Capacity: 600. Tel.: (01203) 385738; (01203) 325281 (Mornings only)

PAGET RANGERS FC
Founded: 1938 Nickname: 'Rangers' Ground: Springfield Road, Walmley, Sutton Coldfield, West Midlands, B76 8SJ. Total Capacity: 3,000 Seating: 250. Tel. No: (0121) 351-1563

RACING CLUB WARWICK FC
Founded: 1919 Nickname: 'Racing' Former Name: Saltisford Rovers FC. Ground: Townend Meadow, Hampton Road, Warwick. Ground Capacity: 1,000 Seating Capacity: 200. Tel. No: (01926) 612675 (Sec.)

REDDITCH UNITED FC
Founded: 1892 Nickname: 'The Reds' Ground: Valley Stadium, Bromsgrove Road, Redditch. Ground Capacity: 7,000 Seating Capacity: 250. Tel. No: (01527) 526603 (Secretary); (01527) 67450 (Ground)

ROTHWELL TOWN FC
Founded: 1956 Nickname: 'Town' Former Name: Rothwell Town Swifts FC. Ground: Cecil Street, Rothwell, Northants. Ground Capacity: 3,000 Seating Capacity: 460. Tel. No: (01536) 710694 (Ground)

SOLIHULL BOROUGH FC
Founded: 1951 Nickname: 'The Boro' Former Name: Lincoln FC Ground: The Moorlands, Sherwood Road, Hall Green, Birmingham. Ground Capacity: 3,250 Seating Capacity: 250 Tel.: (0121) 745-6758 (Club)

STOURBRIDGE FC
Founded: 1876 Nickname: 'The Glassboys' Former Name: Stourbridge Standard FC. Ground: War Memorial Athletic Ground, High Street, Amblecote, Stourbridge DY8 4EB. Ground Capacity: 2,000 Seating Capacity: 260. Tel. No: (01384) 392975 (Secretary)

SUTTON COLDFIELD TOWN FC
Founded: 1879 Nickname: 'The Royals' Former Name: Sutton Town FC. Ground: Central Ground, Coles Lane, Sutton Coldfield, West Midlands B72 1NL. Capacity: 2,000 Seating: 200 Tel.: (0121) 354-2997

Continued on page 101

100

BEAZER HOMES SOUTHERN DIVISION

ASHFORD TOWN FC
Founded: 1930 Nickname: 'Nuts & Bolts' Ground: The Homelands, Ashford Road, Kingsnorth, Ashford, Kent TN26 1NT. Ground Capacity: 3,000 Seating Capacity: 495. Tel. No: (01233) 611838 (Ground)

BASHLEY FC
Founded: 1947 Nickname: 'The Bash' Ground: Recreation Ground, Bashley, Common Road, New Milton, Hants. Ground Capacity: 4,250 Seating Capacity: 400. Tel. No: (01425) 620280 (Ground)

BRAINTREE TOWN FC
Founded: 1898 Nickname: 'The Iron' Former Names: Manor Works FC, Crittall Athletic FC, Braintree & Crittall Athletic FC, Braintree FC, Braintree Town FC. Ground: Cressing Road Stadium, Clockhouse Way, Cressing Road, Braintree, Essex. Ground Capacity: 4,000 Seating Capacity: 292. Tel. No: (01376) 345617

CLEVEDON TOWN FC
Founded: 1880 Ground: The Hand Stadium, Davis Lane, Clevedon, Avon. Ground Capacity: 2,608 Seating Capacity: 293. Tel. No: (01275) 871636 (Club); (01275) 391641 (Office)

ERITH & BELVEDERE FC
Founded: 1908 Nickname: 'The Dere's' Ground: Park View, Lower Road, Belvedere, Kent. Ground Capacity: 1,500 Seating Capacity: 250. Tel. No: (0181) 311-0650

FAREHAM TOWN FC
Founded: 1947 Nickname: 'The Town' Ground: Cams Alders Stadium, Highfield Avenue, Fareham, Hants, PO14 1JA. Ground Capacity: 3,500 Seating Capacity: 450. Tel.: (01329) 231151; (01329) 285432 (Secretary)

FISHER ATHLETIC FC
Founded: 1908 Nickname: 'The Fish' Ground: Surrey Docks Stadium, Salter Road, London, SE16 1LQ. Ground Capacity: 5,700 Seating Capacity: 600. Tel.: (0171) 231-5144 (Office); (0171) 252-0590 (Ground)

FLEET TOWN FC
Founded: 1896 Nickname: 'Town' Ground: Calthorpe Park, Crookham Road, Fleet, Hants. Ground Capacity: 4,000 Seating Capacity: 200. Tel.: (01252) 623804

FOREST GREEN ROVERS FC
Founded: 1890 Nickname: 'The Green' 'The Rovers' Former Name: Stroud FC. Ground: The Lawn, Nympsfield Road, Forest Green, Nailsworth, Stroud, Glos. Total Capacity: 3,008 Seating: 200. Tel. No: (01453) 834860

HAVANT TOWN FC
Founded: 1898 Nickname: 'Town' Former Names: Havant Rovers FC, Havant & Leigh Park FC. Ground: Westleigh Park, Martins Road, Havant, Hants. Ground Capacity: 6,000 Seating Capacity: 275. Tel. No: (01705) 267276 (Secretary)

MARGATE FC
Founded: 1896 Nickname: 'The Gate' Former Name: Thanet United FC. Ground: Hartsdown Park, Hartsdown Road, Margate. Ground Capacity: 6,000 Seating Capacity: 350. Tel. No: (01843) 291040 (Secretary);

(01843) 221769 (Ground)

NEWPORT I.O.W. FC
Founded: 1888 Nickname: 'The Port' Ground: St. George's Park, St. George's Way, Newport, I.O.W. Ground Capacity: 5,000 Seating Capacity: 300. Tel. No: (01983) 525027

POOLE TOWN FC
Founded: 1880 Nickname: 'The Dolphins' Ground: County Ground, Blandford Close, Hamworthy, Poole BH15 4BF. Ground Capacity: 2,500 Seating Capacity: 200. Tel. No: (01202) 536906 (Secretary)

SITTINGBOURNE FC
Founded: 1881 Nickname: 'The Brickies' Ground: Central Park Eurolink, Sittingbourne, Kent, ME10 3SB. Ground Capacity: 7,600 Seating Capacity: 2,000 Tel.: (01795) 475577

TONBRIDGE AFC
Founded: 1948 Ground: Longmead Stadium, Darenth Avenue, Tonbridge, Kent. Ground Capacity: 5,000 Seating Capacity: 200 Tel. No: (01732) 352417

TROWBRIDGE TOWN FC
Founded: 1880 Nickname: 'The Bees' Ground: County Way, Trowbridge, Wilshire. Ground Capacity: 5,000 Seating Capacity: 200. Tel.: (01225) 752076

WATERLOOVILLE FC
Founded: 1905 Nickname: 'The Ville' Ground: Jubilee Park, Aston Road, Waterlooville, Hants. Ground Capacity: 6,000 Seating Capacity: 500. Tel.: (01705) 263867/230114 (Daytime); (01705) 254529 (Evenings)

WESTON-SUPER-MARE AFC
Founded: 1948 Nickname: 'The Seagulls' Ground: Woodspring Park, Winterstoke Road, Weston-Super-Mare, Avon, BS23 2YG. Ground Capacity: 4,000. Seating Capacity: 250. Tel. No: (01934) 621618

WEYMOUTH FC
Founded: 1890 Nickname: 'The Terras' Ground: Wessex Stadium, Radipole Lane, Weymouth, Dorset. Ground Capacity: 9,999 Seating Capacity: 850. Tel. No: (01305) 785558

WITNEY TOWN FC
Founded: 1885 Nickname: 'Town' Ground: Marriotts Stadium, Downs Road, Witney, Oxon, OX8 5LY. Ground Capacity: 3,500 Seating Capacity: 234. Tel. No: (01993) 702549

YATE TOWN FC
Founded: Reformed 1946 Nickname: 'The Bluebells' Former Name: Yate YMCA FC, Yate Rovers FC. Ground: Lodge Road, Yate, Bristol, BS17 5LE. Ground Capacity: 2,000. Seating: 226. Tel. No: (01454) 228103

continued from page 100

TAMWORTH FC
Founded: 1933 Nickname: 'The Lambs' ' The Town' Ground: The Lamb Ground, Kettlebrook, Tamworth B79 1HA. Ground Capacity: 2,500 Seating Capacity: 400. Tel. No: (01827) 65798; (01827) 66786 (Secretary)

GM Vauxhall Conference Season 1994/95	Altrincham	Bath City	Bromsgrove Rovers	Dagenham & Redbridge	Dover Athletic	Farnborough Town	Gateshead	Halifax Town	Kettering Town	Kidderminster Harriers	Macclesfield Town	Merthyr Tydfil	Northwich Victoria	Runcorn	Southport	Stafford Rangers	Stalybridge Celtic	Stevenage Borough	Telford United	Welling United	Woking	Yeovil Town
Altrincham	■	1-0	1-1	0-1	3-0	2-0	1-3	3-1	2-4	2-0	1-2	1-0	1-3	3-2	0-0	5-1	1-0	1-2	3-1	1-1	1-2	1-3
Bath City	0-3	■	1-1	3-0	0-0	2-0	0-2	0-0	2-0	3-5	1-0	1-0	2-2	4-3	1-2	3-3	2-3	2-1	1-1	2-0	2-0	3-0
Bromsgrove Rvrs.	0-3	1-1	■	2-2	2-0	2-2	2-2	0-1	2-4	4-3	2-2	2-0	1-4	1-0	1-1	2-1	2-1	2-1	0-1	4-1	5-5	5-0
Dagenham & R.	0-4	1-0	2-0	■	2-0	0-1	0-0	1-4	2-1	1-2	0-4	2-1	1-2	3-2	5-1	3-3	2-2	0-1	3-2	0-0	0-2	0-0
Dover Athletic	1-3	3-0	0-2	1-1	■	1-1	2-2	1-1	0-2	1-0	0-0	2-2	3-1	1-1	1-2	3-2	0-0	2-0	2-0	1-1	2-3	1-1
Farnborough T.	2-3	0-0	0-3	1-3	1-0	■	3-1	2-0	0-0	1-0	1-0	2-1	2-1	0-4	1-4	0-0	0-0	1-1	5-3	1-2	0-2	0-3
Gateshead	1-0	0-1	2-1	2-1	1-0	2-0	■	1-2	0-0	1-0	2-1	2-0	4-0	4-0	0-1	1-1	0-0	1-2	0-0	2-0	2-0	0-3
Halifax Town	1-1	4-2	4-2	1-1	4-0	0-1	3-2	■	2-1	1-2	0-1	2-2	0-0	4-0	2-0	6-0	1-1	0-2	1-1	4-0	4-0	2-1
Kettering Town	2-2	0-0	0-1	2-2	1-0	4-1	2-4	5-1	■	0-0	1-0	4-1	3-3	3-0	1-0	1-0	1-0	0-2	3-2	4-3	0-1	3-2
Kidderminster H.	2-2	2-1	0-1	1-1	0-0	0-1	2-3	3-0	1-3	■	1-2	2-0	1-2	1-1	0-1	1-2	3-2	0-3	1-1	3-0	1-3	3-0
Macclesfield T.	4-2	1-0	2-2	2-0	3-0	4-1	2-1	1-1	1-0	1-3	■	0-0	3-0	0-1	3-0	1-2	3-0	0-3	2-0	3-1	2-0	1-0
Merthyr Tydfil	2-5	2-0	2-1	2-0	2-3	1-1	1-2	2-0	2-1	0-1	1-2	■	2-0	3-0	1-2	4-1	4-2	2-2	3-1	0-2	1-1	0-0
Northwich Vict.	1-1	1-1	3-1	5-0	1-3	1-2	1-1	3-0	3-2	3-4	1-3	2-0	■	4-1	2-1	0-1	2-2	0-1	1-1	1-1	2-2	2-2
Runcorn	3-0	1-1	3-1	0-0	3-3	1-0	3-2	0-3	1-2	2-2	2-2	0-0	2-2	■	2-1	3-1	0-3	3-1	4-1	3-2	1-0	2-1
Southport	1-4	3-1	2-1	1-1	2-2	0-1	5-0	4-0	1-0	4-1	2-3	3-1	0-2	5-0	■	3-0	3-1	2-1	2-1	1-0	2-0	0-0
Stafford Rangers	0-1	0-2	1-1	1-2	1-0	1-1	3-1	0-1	2-3	1-2	0-3	2-0	1-3	1-2	1-1	■	5-0	0-3	2-2	1-1	2-3	4-1
Stalybridge Celtic	2-1	0-1	1-1	1-0	2-1	4-1	0-1	1-1	1-4	1-3	2-2	1-1	2-1	0-0	1-1	2-3	■	1-0	1-0	1-3	2-1	3-1
Stevenage Boro'	4-2	3-0	1-0	3-1	0-3	3-1	2-3	1-0	2-2	2-3	1-1	0-0	1-1	0-1	1-2	1-0	5-1	■	4-3	1-2	0-1	5-0
Telford United	2-3	3-0	2-2	0-4	1-1	1-1	3-1	1-1	1-0	3-1	2-0	1-1	1-0	2-0	0-0	0-0	1-1	1-2	■	4-2	0-0	1-0
Welling United	0-0	1-5	1-2	4-1	0-1	1-3	3-0	1-1	2-1	0-2	0-1	2-1	1-5	1-2	3-1	3-1	3-3	1-0	1-0	■	1-2	2-1
Woking	4-0	2-2	4-0	3-5	0-0	3-2	1-1	1-3	3-1	0-0	1-0	4-1	1-0	2-0	3-0	2-2	4-1	3-0	2-1	1-1	■	2-2
Yeovil Town	1-3	1-2	2-0	2-2	1-3	0-1	1-1	3-1	1-1	1-1	1-2	1-3	4-4	1-0	0-1	1-0	3-0	0-0	1-1	3-3	1-2	■

GM VAUXHALL CONFERENCE 1994/95

FINAL LEAGUE TABLE

Macclesfield Town	42	24	8	10	70	40	80
Woking	42	21	12	9	76	54	75
Southport	42	21	9	12	68	50	72
Altrincham Town	42	20	8	14	77	60	68
Stevenage Borough	42	20	7	15	68	49	67
Kettering Town	42	19	10	13	73	56	67
Gateshead	42	19	10	13	61	53	67
Halifax Town	42	17	12	13	68	54	63
Runcorn	42	16	10	16	59	71	58
Northwich Victoria	42	14	15	13	77	66	57
Kidderminster Harr.	42	16	9	17	63	61	57
Bath City	42	15	12	15	55	56	57
Bromsgrove Rovers	42	14	3	15	66	69	55
Farnborough Town	42	15	10	17	45	64	55
Dag'ham & R'bridge	42	13	13	16	56	69	52
Dover Athletic	42	11	16	15	48	55	49
Welling United	42	13	10	19	57	74	49
Stalybridge Celtic	42	11	14	17	52	72	47
Telford United	42	10	16	16	53	62	46
Merthyr Tydfil	42	11	11	20	53	63	44
Stafford Rangers	42	9	11	22	53	79	38
* Yeovil Town	42	8	14	20	50	71	37

* Yeovil Town had one point deducted for fielding an ineligible player

Champions : - Macclesfield Town

Relegated : - Merthyr Tydfil, Stafford Rangers & Yeovil Town

Diadora League Premier Division Season 1994/95	Aylesbury United	Bishop's Stortford	Bromley	Carshalton Athletic	Chesham United	Dulwich Hamlet	Enfield	Grays Athletic	Harrow Borough	Hayes	Hendon	Hitchin Town	Kingstonian	Marlow	Molesey	Purfleet	Slough Town	St. Albans City	Sutton United	Walton & Hersham	Wokingham Town	Yeading
Aylesbury Utd.		3-0	3-2	5-0	5-1	5-3	3-3	2-0	3-0	2-0	1-0	2-1	2-0	0-0	2-4	1-1	3-3	0-0	3-0	4-0	4-1	1-2
Bishop's St'ford	2-1		2-1	3-4	0-3	3-3	1-1	0-1	0-2	2-2	1-2	1-0	2-1	2-0	3-1	2-5	2-2	1-2	1-1	0-2	5-1	2-0
Bromley	3-2	0-1		0-1	1-3	0-2	2-0	2-1	1-0	2-0	1-1	0-2	3-1	0-6	4-3	2-2	1-1	2-2	4-4	5-0	3-1	3-1
Carshalton Ath.	1-3	1-2	0-3		1-1	2-1	1-3	0-1	3-4	0-0	3-0	2-4	0-0	3-1	2-0	2-2	1-3	2-0	2-1	1-0	2-2	1-1
Chesham United	0-2	1-1	0-3	6-2		2-1	0-3	1-1	2-0	2-3	3-1	2-2	0-5	1-0	0-3	1-1	0-1	1-6	1-3	1-0	5-1	1-1
Dulwich Hamlet	4-3	0-2	2-2	1-2	1-0		1-2	1-1	2-3	4-2	1-0	0-1	1-5	3-2	3-2	2-2	0-2	4-1	4-2	4-3	1-1	1-3
Enfield	2-2	1-0	3-1	2-1	1-1	8-1		2-1	3-0	0-1	5-1	4-1	1-1	5-0	1-1	3-1	0-1	3-1	2-1	1-1	6-0	3-0
Grays Athletic	0-2	2-3	0-3	3-4	5-0	0-0	2-3		1-1	0-3	2-1	1-3	0-0	2-1	0-0	1-2	3-3	2-2	2-2	1-1	2-0	1-3
Harrow	3-0	2-0	2-0	2-1	1-0	1-2	0-1	1-2		0-1	2-4	2-4	1-1	3-1	5-2	3-5	0-3	2-1	1-3	4-2	3-0	1-1
Hayes	2-0	1-0	2-2	5-0	2-0	1-1	1-4	1-2	1-1		1-1	0-0	1-0	2-0	3-2	4-1	3-1	1-1	2-1	2-0	1-0	1-3
Hendon	2-1	1-1	1-1	0-1	2-1	4-0	1-3	3-3	1-2	0-0		4-1	0-0	3-0	3-1	1-0	1-2	1-1	0-1	1-6	2-0	2-2
Hitchin Town	3-1	1-1	3-3	0-1	4-3	0-1	0-3	0-0	0-0	0-0	2-0		1-1	4-2	1-3	3-2	1-0	2-0	1-1	3-1	1-0	1-3
Kingstonian	2-0	1-0	1-0	0-1	5-1	5-3	3-2	1-0	3-1	1-1	1-2	3-1		2-1	0-1	0-1	0-3	3-5	1-1	2-5	5-0	0-1
Marlow	3-2	3-1	1-2	1-1	1-4	0-4	2-2	1-4	2-0	1-3	0-0	0-4	1-0		3-0	1-0	0-2	4-4	1-3	2-2	1-1	1-0
Molesey	1-3	4-0	1-1	4-1	1-2	1-0	0-2	1-1	2-0	0-2	1-1	0-0	1-2	2-1		1-2	0-2	3-2	1-1	2-1	1-0	1-0
Purfleet	0-3	3-3	2-1	4-4	3-1	1-2	2-2	0-3	4-2	1-2	3-3	1-3	0-3	3-1	0-1		3-0	0-4	2-2	2-5	4-3	2-2
Slough Town	1-0	1-0	4-1	3-3	5-2	1-1	1-4	2-0	1-1	3-1	2-2	3-2	2-1	4-0	3-1	2-4		1-1	3-2	0-0	1-0	5-3
St. Albans	2-1	5-0	1-2	3-1	4-2	3-2	1-2	1-1	1-0	1-1	3-2	3-3	8-3	3-2	0-2	2-0	3-1		3-2	2-2	6-2	1-1
Sutton United	1-3	5-0	1-2	3-2	1-2	4-2	0-2	2-2	2-1	3-3	3-1	0-0	4-1	1-2	2-3	1-2	1-1	5-1		0-0	0-2	2-0
Walton & Hersh.	2-0	5-2	2-3	2-4	1-1	4-1	1-3	2-1	1-2	3-1	2-0	4-1	0-2	1-1	1-2	2-2	3-3	3-2	1-0		0-1	1-1
Wokingham Tn.	0-1	0-0	1-1	2-3	2-1	0-1	0-3	0-1	0-2	1-2	1-1	1-3	0-1	1-2	1-1	5-1	2-0	2-2	0-1	3-2		0-3
Yeading	4-2	1-1	1-3	3-2	1-1	1-1	4-2	1-1	0-3	1-1	0-1	0-1	1-0	0-0	0-4	1-0	0-0	7-2	2-1	0-1	1-1	

DIADORA PREMIER DIVISION 1994/95

FINAL LEAGUE TABLE

Enfield	42	28	9	5	106	43	93
Slough Town	42	22	13	7	82	56	79
Hayes	42	20	14	8	66	47	74
Aylesbury United	42	21	6	15	86	59	69
Hitchin Town	42	18	12	12	68	59	66
Bromley	42	18	11	13	76	67	65
St. Albans City	42	17	13	12	96	81	64
Molesey	42	18	8	16	65	61	62
Yeading	42	14	15	13	60	59	57
Harrow Borough	42	17	6	19	74	67	57
Dulwich Hamlet	42	16	9	17	70	82	57
Carshalton Athletic	42	16	9	17	69	84	57
Kingstonian	42	16	8	18	62	57	56
Walton & Hersham	42	14	11	17	75	73	53
Sutton United	42	13	12	17	74	69	51
Purfleet	42	13	12	17	76	90	51
Hendon	42	12	14	16	57	65	50
Grays Athletic	42	11	16	15	57	61	49
Bishop's Stortford	42	12	11	19	53	76	47
Chesham United	42	12	9	21	60	87	45
Marlow	42	10	9	23	52	84	39
Wokingham Town	42	6	9	27	39	86	27

Promoted : - Slough Town
Relegated : - Chesham United, Marlow, Wokingham Town

Unibond North. Premier League Premier Division Season 1994/95	Accrington Stanley	Barrow	Bishop Auckland	Boston United	Buxton	Chorley	Colwyn Bay	Droylsden	Emley	Frickley Athletic	Gainsborough Trinity	Guiseley	Horwich RMI	Hyde United	Knowsley United	Marine	Matlock Town	Morecambe	Spennymoor United	Whitley Bay	Winsford United	Witton Albion
Accrington Stan.		5-2	1-4	0-4	1-0	1-1	1-3	2-1	1-1	1-1	1-2	1-4	3-0	1-0	2-2	1-5	0-2	0-4	0-1	4-1	2-2	1-2
Barrow	2-2		2-1	2-5	4-2	2-1	5-0	1-1	1-0	1-2	1-0	2-3	1-0	1-1	2-3	0-3	3-1	0-1	1-1	4-0	2-1	0-1
Bishop Auckland	2-0	3-0		0-0	2-2	2-2	3-3	0-1	2-2	2-0	1-1	0-1	2-1	0-2	0-2	0-1	3-1	0-3	0-0	2-2	2-1	0-1
Boston United	4-2	3-1	1-2		0-1	2-0	5-2	5-1	1-2	5-0	2-2	2-2	4-0	2-1	6-1	1-1	2-0	0-2	2-3	2-1	0-0	1-1
Buxton	0-1	1-0	2-2	0-0		1-2	4-2	2-2	0-1	3-2	0-4	3-2	4-0	1-2	1-0	0-2	4-0	1-2	3-0	2-1	1-1	1-1
Chorley	1-2	3-1	1-1	0-1	0-1		3-2	2-4	2-3	2-3	0-2	2-4	2-3	1-0	3-1	1-4	0-1	1-4	1-2	1-4	2-0	0-2
Colwyn Bay	3-3	1-2	1-3	0-1	1-2	3-2		3-2	3-0	1-2	0-0	2-4	3-1	1-0	1-1	0-1	0-4	0-0	2-1	5-1	1-0	2-2
Droylsden	1-3	1-0	1-4	1-0	1-2	0-0	1-3		0-0	2-1	2-6	1-3	2-1	3-3	1-3	1-4	3-2	3-2	1-2	0-1	5-1	0-2
Emley	0-0	2-1	1-4	1-4	2-0	1-4	1-0	3-1		2-0	3-2	1-0	1-1	1-3	3-3	0-0	0-1	0-0	5-1	4-0	1-1	0-0
Frickley Athletic	1-1	1-2	2-2	1-1	1-1	3-3	1-2	2-0	3-2		1-2	2-1	1-2	1-2	2-2	0-1	0-1	1-4	0-2	1-5	3-0	2-2
Gainsborough T.	0-1	4-3	2-2	2-0	0-2	3-2	6-1	2-2	3-0	1-1		0-1	1-0	1-1	2-1	0-0	3-2	0-0	0-3	2-2	1-1	1-0
Guiseley	4-0	2-1	2-1	2-1	3-1	2-1	3-2	2-0	2-0	2-1	1-0		1-2	3-3	5-0	2-1	3-0	2-2	1-1	6-3	5-1	1-1
Horwich RMI	1-5	1-6	0-2	0-4	4-1	6-0	0-1	2-2	4-4	0-3	2-1	0-2		0-1	1-2	1-4	0-3	0-2	0-0	2-3	1-0	0-1
Hyde United	4-1	3-1	1-0	1-0	4-2	2-3	4-3	5-2	1-1	6-0	5-1	1-2	2-1		3-0	1-2	6-3	1-4	1-1	3-0	1-2	2-1
Knowsley United	0-0	0-2	2-3	2-2	1-3	1-2	2-2	3-0	4-2	0-3	4-2	2-1	2-1	1-2		1-1	0-0	1-1	2-0	3-0	0-5	1-4
Marine	2-1	4-0	2-0	2-1	1-1	3-1	1-0	4-1	2-1	2-0	1-4	1-1	2-0	1-1	1-0		3-0	2-1	1-0	2-0	2-1	4-1
Matlock Town	0-1	1-1	4-0	0-1	2-1	2-2	1-2	3-2	5-1	0-2	2-1	2-3	3-2	0-1	3-3	0-0		0-2	1-2	5-1	0-2	0-1
Morecambe	3-0	1-3	1-0	2-1	1-1	2-0	1-1	4-0	2-1	3-1	4-0	2-2	7-1	1-3	1-1	0-0	5-0		3-2	2-0	6-1	5-2
Spennymoor Utd.	5-1	0-1	1-0	1-1	4-1	2-2	5-2	2-1	2-1	2-0	1-1	1-1	2-1	1-1	2-1	0-3	2-1	1-3		4-0	1-1	2-1
Whitley Bay	0-0	3-1	1-4	0-1	1-3	2-1	0-2	0-1	0-3	2-2	2-2	0-1	0-3	2-2	5-3	0-4	0-2	0-2	1-0		0-1	1-1
Winsford United	2-2	3-0	0-4	1-2	1-2	1-3	0-1	2-1	2-3	2-0	2-0	2-2	2-3	5-1	2-2	2-2	2-4	0-2	1-2	1-1		1-0
Witton Albion	0-0	0-3	1-3	0-0	1-2	1-4	1-4	1-1	2-2	2-0	1-2	1-2	2-1	2-2	1-1	1-1	2-0	1-2	2-1	3-0	2-0	

UNIBOND NORTHERN PREMIER LEAGUE
PREMIER DIVISION SEASON 1994/95
FINAL LEAGUE TABLE

Marine	42	29	11	2	83	27	98
Morecambe	42	28	10	4	99	34	94
Guiseley	42	28	9	5	96	50	93
Hyde United	42	22	10	10	89	59	76
Boston United	42	20	11	11	80	43	71
Spennymoor United	42	20	11	11	66	52	71
Buxton	42	18	9	15	65	62	63
Gainsborough Trinity	42	16	13	13	69	61	61
Bishop Auckland	42	16	12	14	68	55	60
Witton Albion	42	14	14	14	54	56	56
Barrow	42	17	5	20	68	71	56
Colwyn Bay	42	16	8	18	71	80	56
Emley	42	14	13	15	62	68	55
Matlock Town	42	15	5	22	62	72	50
Accrington Stanley	42	12	13	17	51	77	49
Knowsley United	42	11	14	17	64	83	47
Winsford United	42	10	11	21	56	75	41
Chorley	42	11	7	24	64	87	40
Frickley Athletic	42	10	10	22	53	79	40
Droylsden	42	10	8	24	56	93	38
Whitley Bay	42	8	8	26	46	97	32
Horwich R.M.I.	42	9	4	29	49	94	31

Promoted : - Morecambe
Relegated : - Whitley Bay & Horwich R.M.I.

Beazer Homes Premier Division Season 1994/95	Atherstone United	Burton Albion	Cambridge City	Chelmsford City	Cheltenham Town	Corby Town	Crawley Town	Dorchester Town	Gloucester City	Gravesend & Northfleet	Gresley Rovers	Halesowen Town	Hastings Town	Hednesford Town	Leek Town	Rushden & Diamonds	Sittingbourne	Solihull Borough	Sudbury Town	Trowbridge Town	V.S. Rugby	Worcester City
Atherstone Utd.	■	1-2	0-2	1-1	2-4	4-0	0-0	0-1	1-0	3-0	1-2	1-1	1-3	1-3	1-1	1-7	3-1	2-0	3-0	1-2	1-1	0-0
Burton Albion	1-1	■	0-0	2-1	2-0	3-2	1-0	1-1	0-1	2-1	2-1	0-0	1-1	2-4	1-1	2-2	1-0	2-0	1-1	2-0	3-1	0-1
Cambridge City	0-2	2-0	■	1-0	0-1	2-1	2-1	2-1	0-1	1-0	0-1	2-2	1-0	1-1	5-1	2-3	4-1	2-4	1-1	4-0	2-0	0-2
Chelmsford City	4-1	0-4	2-0	■	1-2	5-0	1-2	3-1	0-2	1-2	2-4	4-3	0-0	1-2	2-2	2-2	2-1	3-1	1-0	0-1	3-2	1-0
Cheltenham Tn.	2-2	1-2	1-1	1-0	■	8-0	1-2	1-1	1-1	2-0	1-1	3-0	6-0	2-0	1-0	3-0	2-1	2-0	3-0	3-2	1-0	1-1
Corby Town	0-0	1-1	1-2	1-4	2-2	■	1-1	2-4	0-6	0-2	1-2	0-2	1-1	3-1	0-1	0-4	2-1	1-2	3-4	1-1	1-0	2-1
Crawley Town	2-1	3-4	1-0	1-0	1-1	2-2	■	2-1	0-1	1-2	1-1	5-1	5-2	2-4	0-1	2-4	2-0	0-1	2-0	4-2	1-0	1-0
Dorchester Tn.	2-3	0-1	0-1	1-0	1-4	5-0	5-2	■	4-2	4-5	1-1	3-1	3-1	0-0	2-1	4-2	3-1	1-1	3-0	1-3	3-1	1-1
Gloucester City	4-0	1-0	5-1	2-0	1-2	2-2	4-1	0-3	■	3-3	3-3	1-2	1-0	2-2	2-0	1-0	0-0	1-2	3-0	2-0	3-0	1-2
Gr'send & N'flt.	2-1	0-1	1-1	1-0	0-1	1-0	0-2	2-1	1-0	■	1-0	1-1	0-0	0-0	1-1	0-1	1-1	0-0	3-0	0-0	0-0	0-0
Gresley Rovers	1-2	1-1	3-1	1-0	1-4	1-0	2-4	1-3	3-2	0-0	■	3-2	3-2	1-2	2-1	4-3	1-1	5-1	0-1	5-1	2-2	0-0
Halesowen Tn.	3-0	0-1	1-0	3-2	1-1	4-1	2-2	2-5	1-1	4-1	1-4	■	1-2	1-2	4-5	2-4	3-0	4-2	5-1	2-0	5-0	0-3
Hastings Town	3-1	1-1	4-3	0-1	3-1	1-1	2-2	2-1	2-1	1-2	2-0	3-1	■	0-0	1-2	0-2	1-1	3-0	4-1	1-0	1-1	1-1
Hednesford Tn.	6-1	5-1	2-1	2-1	3-1	4-1	2-1	0-0	1-3	5-1	2-1	3-2	2-1	■	3-0	5-2	2-1	5-0	1-1	4-1	2-0	1-1
Leek Town	2-1	0-1	4-1	0-3	1-3	6-1	3-0	4-5	3-1	2-0	1-1	3-0	1-0	1-3	■	3-3	2-0	0-1	4-1	3-0	0-0	0-0
Rushden & Diam.	2-2	2-2	2-1	3-1	0-2	6-1	5-0	2-1	1-2	6-2	0-1	1-1	3-1	2-3	5-0	■	5-0	3-1	2-2	2-1	4-1	1-1
Sittingbourne	1-0	0-2	1-1	2-3	0-3	4-0	3-1	1-2	2-1	4-0	0-0	3-2	2-1	3-2	0-0	3-1	■	2-1	0-4	4-1	1-1	1-2
Solihull Borough	0-1	1-1	0-2	1-1	0-0	0-0	1-1	2-4	1-2	0-0	0-0	2-2	1-3	2-2	1-2	0-0	2-1	■	1-1	1-0	0-3	1-0
Sudbury Town	0-2	0-1	1-2	1-0	1-5	5-1	0-0	1-1	0-1	2-1	0-4	1-0	3-2	1-3	1-0	2-2	0-1		■	2-4	3-0	0-0
Trowbridge Tn.	0-0	0-0	1-2	1-0	1-2	2-0	1-1	1-1	1-2	2-0	3-2	2-2	0-0	1-2	1-1	1-1	1-1	0-0	4-3	■	1-3	0-1
V.S. Rugby	1-1	0-0	1-1	0-0	2-0	3-0	3-1	1-0	3-3	0-2	6-3	0-2	0-0	0-3	1-3	2-0	2-0	2-3	2-2	0-0	■	2-0
Worcester City	0-1	1-0	1-3	3-0	2-2	3-0	4-2	0-0	0-1	1-0	0-1	3-1	1-1	0-1	1-3	1-1	4-0	1-1	0-1	3-0	0-1	■

BEAZER HOMES LEAGUE
PREMIER DIVISION 1994/95
FINAL LEAGUE TABLE

Hednesford Town	42	28	9	5	99	49	93
Cheltenham Town	42	25	11	6	87	39	86
Burton Albion	42	20	15	7	55	39	75
Gloucester City	42	22	8	12	76	48	74
Rushden & Diamonds	42	19	11	12	99	65	68
Dorchester Town	42	19	10	13	84	61	67
Leek Town	42	19	10	13	72	60	67
Gresley Rovers	42	17	12	13	70	63	63
Cambridge City	42	18	8	16	60	55	62
Worcester City	42	14	15	13	46	34	57
Crawley Town	42	15	10	17	64	71	55
Hastings Town	42	13	14	15	55	57	53
Halesowen Town	42	14	10	18	81	80	52
Gravesend & N'fleet	42	13	13	16	38	55	52
Chelmsford City	42	14	6	22	56	60	48
Atherstone United	42	12	12	18	51	67	48
V. S. Rugby	42	11	14	17	49	61	47
Sudbury Town	42	12	10	20	50	77	46
Solihull Borough	42	10	15	17	39	65	45
Sittingbourne	42	11	10	21	51	73	43
Trowbridge Town	42	9	13	20	43	69	40
* Corby Town	42	4	10	28	36	113	21

* Corby Town had one point deducted for fielding ineligible players

Promoted : - Hednesford Town

Relegated : - Solihull Borough, Sittingbourne, Trowbridge Town & Corby Town

BEAZER HOMES LEAGUE
MIDLAND DIVISION SEASON 1994/95
FINAL LEAGUE TABLE

Newport AFC	42	29	8	5	106	39	95
Ilkeston Town	42	25	6	11	101	75	81
Tamworth	42	24	8	10	98	70	80
Moor Green	42	23	8	11	105	63	77
Bridgnorth Town	42	22	10	10	75	49	76
Buckingham Town	42	20	14	8	55	37	74
Nuneaton Borough	42	19	11	12	76	55	68
Rothwell Town	42	19	7	16	71	71	64
King's Lynn	42	18	8	16	76	64	62
R. C. Warwick	42	17	11	14	68	63	62
Dudley Town	42	17	10	15	65	69	61
Bilston Town	42	17	8	17	73	64	59
Bedworth United	42	17	7	18	64	68	58
Evesham United	42	14	10	18	57	56	52
Hinckley Town	42	14	10	18	61	76	52
Stourbridge	42	15	7	20	59	77	52
Sutton Coldfield Town	42	12	10	20	62	72	46
Forest Green Rovers	42	11	13	18	56	76	46
Redditch United	42	8	14	20	47	64	38
Leicester United	42	10	8	24	51	99	38
Grantham Town	42	8	9	25	55	93	33
Armitage	42	2	5	35	35	116	11

Promoted : - Newport AFC & Ilkeston Town
Relegated : - Armitage

BEAZER HOMES LEAGUE
SOUTHERN DIVISION 1994/95 SEASON
FINAL LEAGUE TABLE

Salisbury City	42	30	7	5	88	37	97
Baldock Town	42	28	10	4	92	44	94
Havant Town	42	25	10	7	81	34	85
Waterlooville	42	24	8	10	77	36	80
Ashford Town	42	21	12	9	106	72	75
Weston-Super-Mare	42	18	13	11	82	54	67
Bashley	42	18	11	13	62	49	65
Weymouth	42	16	13	13	60	55	61
Newport IOW	42	17	10	15	67	67	61
Witney Town	42	14	14	14	57	57	56
Clevedon Town	42	14	13	15	73	64	55
Tonbridge Angels	42	14	12	16	74	87	54
Margate	42	15	7	20	60	72	52
Braintree Town	42	12	13	17	64	71	49
Wealdstone	42	13	8	21	76	94	47
Yate Town	42	11	13	18	57	75	46
Fisher 93	42	9	16	17	54	70	43
Bury Town	42	11	8	23	59	86	41
Erith & Belvedere	42	10	9	23	49	94	39
Poole Town	42	10	8	24	53	79	38
Fareham Town	42	10	8	24	46	91	38
Burnham	42	7	7	28	40	89	28

Promoted : - Salisbury City & Baldock Town
Relegated : - Burnham

Wealdstone have resigned

NORTHERN LEAGUE DIVISION ONE
SEASON 1994/95
FINAL LEAGUE TABLE

Tow Law Town	38	28	6	4	105	39	90	
Billingham Synthonia	38	23	7	8	99	35	76	
Whitby Town	38	22	10	6	88	45	76	
Bedlington Terriers	38	21	12	5	72	35	75	
RTM Newcastle	38	21	9	8	93	42	72	
Guisborough Town	38	19	11	8	79	48	68	
Durham City	38	17	12	9	75	45	63	
Dunston Fed. Brewery	38	16	12	10	70	62	60	
Consett	38	15	11	12	74	55	56	
Shildon	38	12	13	13	57	83	49	
Hebburn	38	14	9	15	57	68	48	*
West Auckland Town	38	13	8	17	47	61	47	
Seaham Red Star	38	14	6	18	72	72	45	*
Peterlee Newtown	38	12	9	17	62	80	45	
Murton	38	10	5	23	48	89	45	
Chester-le-Street	38	8	7	23	57	99	31	
Ferryhill Athletic	38	9	6	23	34	80	30	*
Eppleton CW	38	8	4	26	38	97	28	
Northallerton Town	38	9	3	26	35	93	27	*
Prudhoe Town	38	6	6	26	39	93	24	

* Hebburn, Seaham Red Star, Ferryhill Athletic and Northallerton Town had 3 points deducted

Relegated : - Northallerton Town & Prudhoe Town

CARLING NORTH WEST COUNTIES DIVISION ONE SEASON 1994/95
FINAL LEAGUE TABLE

Bradford Park Avenue	42	30	4	8	96	43	94
Clitheroe	42	27	9	6	104	49	90
St. Helens Town	42	27	8	7	86	42	89
Trafford	42	27	5	10	98	50	86
Newcastle Town	42	24	7	11	75	57	79
Glossop North End	42	23	8	11	88	59	77
Blackpool Rovers	42	22	7	13	81	64	73
Burscough	42	19	15	8	102	65	72
Prescot	42	16	8	18	47	47	56
Penrith	42	16	7	19	72	72	55
Chadderton	42	15	7	20	56	70	52
Maine Road	42	14	9	19	68	81	51
Eastwood Hanley	42	14	8	20	75	81	50
Holker Old Boys	42	13	11	18	63	72	50
Kidsgrove Athletic	42	14	8	20	66	78	50
Nantwich Town	42	14	7	21	85	83	49
Darwen	42	14	5	23	65	82	47
Rossendale United	42	12	11	19	60	82	47
Bootle	42	11	10	21	46	68	43
Skelmersdale United	42	10	7	25	67	118	37
Salford City	42	9	9	24	45	85	36
Bacup Borough	42	3	6	33	35	132	15

Promoted : - Bradford Park Avenue
Relegated : - Bacup Borough

NORTHERN COUNTIES EAST LEAGUE PREMIER DIVISION SEASON 1994/95
FINAL LEAGUE TABLE

Lincoln United	38	29	5	4	116	49	92
Arnold Town	38	25	7	6	98	46	82
Stocksbridge PS	38	21	6	11	74	46	69
Belper Town	38	19	8	11	78	44	65
Ashfield United	38	18	11	9	65	48	65
Pickering Town	38	19	7	12	89	63	64
North Ferriby United	38	18	8	12	68	60	62
Armthorpe Welfare	38	13	18	7	56	41	57
Thackley	38	15	11	12	76	56	56
Ossett Albion	38	15	9	14	48	57	54
Brigg Town	38	14	10	14	49	57	52
Ossett Town	38	12	10	16	50	56	46
Maltby MW	38	13	7	18	59	71	46
Denaby United	38	12	9	17	48	77	45
Hucknall Town	38	9	13	16	47	60	40
Glasshoughton Welf.	38	10	9	19	60	68	39
Hallam	38	9	8	21	46	76	35
Sheffield	38	6	12	20	45	87	30
Liversedge	38	7	8	23	48	81	29
Pontefract Collieries	38	3	10	25	30	107	19

Promoted : - Lincoln United

THE PREMIERSHIP AND FOOTBALL LEAGUE GROUNDS

… the book everyone has been waiting for : -

Premiership And 1st Division Football Grounds Before And After Taylor

Featuring FOUR postcard-size full-colour photographs of views from the stands of each Premiership and Endsleigh League 1st Division club - two each from 1991 and 1995.

Printed on high quality art paper
Softback Price £9.99
PUBLISHED OCTOBER 1995

Available from your local bookshop or directly from : -
SOCCER BOOK PUBLISHING LIMITED
(Dept. SBP)
72 St. Peter's Avenue, Cleethorpes, South Humberside, DN35 8HU, ENGLAND
Tel. (01472) 601893   FAX. (01472) 698546
(Postage   £1.00 UK : £1.50 Overseas : £4.00 Airmail)